• Basic Instructions and Special Tips •

Ask your friends and family to join you in 'Hands On' crafting fun and you'll soon see how easy it is to double the fun and creativity when you're crafting together...

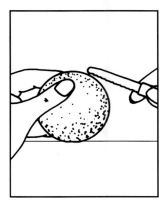

1. Styrofoam can be cut easily by rubbing the edge of a plastic knife with an old wax candle. Cut through the foam with a sawing motion. Use a scrap piece of the Styrofoam to 'sand' any rough edges.

2. IMPORTANT! When you see the 'helping hand' symbol on a project page, it means you may need adult supervision to do the project. Always use care when using tools or a heat source. Be careful and safe!

3. Trace the patterns as needed onto the tracing paper. Lay the traced pattern on top of project surface. Place transfer, or graphite paper under the pattern then trace over design with a soft pencil, or crayon.

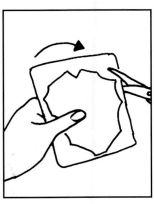

4. When cutting with a pair of scissors, always work slowly and evenly. Hold the material you are cutting with the opposite hand, turning it toward the scissors as you cut.

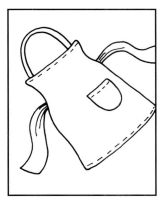

5. When painting or working with messy materials, don't forget to protect your work surface with plastic or newspaper and your clothes with an apron or old shirt. Keep a roll of paper towels handy to wipe up spills.

6. To make sure paint doesn't seep through the shirts or fabric, use a piece of cardboard or wax paper inside the shirt or under fabric while painting. Tape the sleeves and excess shirt together at the back of the board.

7. There are some basic supplies that are used throughout the book which are not always in the project supply list. Some of these general supplies are: paper clips, toothpicks, paper, tracing paper etc.

8. For best results, always read and follow directions given on each product label. Some products may seem to do the same thing, but there may be important differences you need to know.

Hands On Crafts for Kids 3

• TABLE OF CONTENTS •

With spectacular gorges, deserts, salt lakes, caves and an astonishing variety of wildlife, the Outback of Australia is one of the world's last great wilderness areas. The landscape varies from region to region so we concentrate on the style of the Aborigines, the first, nomadic inhabitants of the Outback.

Dilly Bag and Message Stick - Pocket Pal - Aboriginal Oil Pastel
Aboriginal Punched Bolo - Crocodile Candle

Home to the most diverse and complex systems of life on earth, more than $3/4$ of the known species of plants and animals are found in these tropical paradises. They are situated near the equator in Latin America, Africa and Asia. Rain forests occupy 6% of the earth's land mass. The rain forest is known for high temperatures and frequent rainfall producing a hothouse effect. Layers of vegetation are another characteristic leading to its great diversity of species.

Woven Wall Hanging - Leaf Print Floor Cloth - Feathered Mask
Toucan Candy Holder - Palm Tree

The earth is home to a multitude of plants and animals. Man is the biggest threat to the existence of these species. Changes in the environment of these plants and animals often cause their numbers to dwindle and they become endangered. If conservation methods are not used, these species can become extinct.

Endangered Animal Banner - Endangered Animal Flip Book
Pull Toy - Elephant Family - Whooping Crane

This is one habitat that occurs in every part of the world with different plants found in different climates. Our garden program centers on the plants and insects of a typical back yard garden in North America.

Seed Greeting Card - Flower Whirligig - Bumble Bee Mobile
Painted Watering Can - Clothespin Bugs

Deserts make up $1/7$th of the earth's surface. The Sahara is the largest of the 12 main desert regions. Deserts are formed by a particular combination of rainfall, temperatures, location and landscape. All have less than 10" of rain annually. Believe it or not, deserts are a lot more than just sand!

Desert Cactus - Coral Snake - Gemstones
Sand Painted Dunes - Lizard

Dilly Bag and Message Stick

by Patty Cox

Aborigine women wove bags from grasses to carry fish and other foods. Men and boys carried sticks with carved designs to other territories to deliver messages. An identifying mark, such as a tribal design was carved into the stick. Our bag is made from clay and oil pastels.

You will need:	Rolling pin
Oven bake clay	Cookie sheet
6" square of burlap	Oven
Oil pastel - Red Ochre	Wax paper
Hemp cord	Plastic knife
Clear acrylic finish	Metal teaspoon
Toothpick	Paintbrush

Dilly Bag

1. Soften modeling clay in your palms. Place the clay between two sheets of wax paper then press with a rolling pin until it is about $\frac{1}{8}$" thick. To add a woven texture, place a piece of burlap onto the clay. Roll over the burlap with rolling pin then remove the burlap.

2. Place the paper pattern on the clay then use the knife to cut dilly bag front and back pieces.

3. Sandwich clay front and back piece over a teaspoon. The widest part of the spoon should stick out of the bag top. Crimp and pinch clay sides together with your fingers.

4. Poke holes in top sides of bag with a toothpick. Place clay dilly bag with inserted spoon on cookie sheet. Bake at 275° for 10 minutes. Allow the clay to cool completely then remove the spoon.

5. Color clay with an oil pastel by rubbing the color onto the surface with your thumbs. The color will remain in the textured areas. Coat the surface with acrylic finish.

6. Thread hemp cord through each hole. Tie the ends together.

DILLY BAG PATTERN

Cut 2 from clay

Sakura of America Cray-Pas® Junior Artist Oil Pastels;
Delta Ceramcoat® Exterior/Interior Matte Varnish; Darice® Hemp Cording

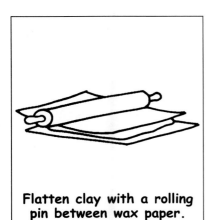

Flatten clay with a rolling pin between wax paper.

Press burlap onto surface of clay with a rolling pin.

Place pattern on clay then cut out with plastic knife.

Press dilly bag pieces together around a spoon.

You will need:
Oven bake clay
Oil pastel - Red Ochre
Natural hemp cord
Clear acrylic finish
Toothpick
Cookie sheet
Oven
Paint brush

Message Stick

1. Soften modeling clay in your palms. Roll clay into a 1" x ½" log. Press the log almost flat, then shape into a long oval. Make a hole in one end with a toothpick.

2. Draw the design on the clay with a toothpick. Make a row of several tiny dots by pressing the toothpick into the clay. Place on a cookie sheet.

3. Bake in an oven at 275° for 10 minutes. Allow clay to cool before next step.

4. Color clay with an oil pastel, rubbing the color into the textured design. Rub color into clay with your thumbs. The color will remain in the dotted lines. Coat with acrylic finish.

5. Thread both ends of the hemp cord through hole then tie a lark's head knot. Knot the ends.

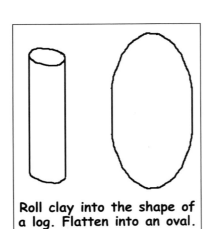

Roll clay into the shape of a log. Flatten into an oval.

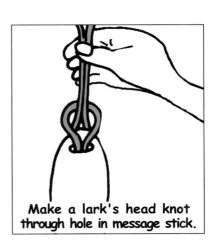

Make a lark's head knot through hole in message stick.

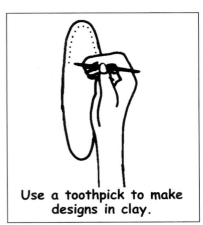

Use a toothpick to make designs in clay.

Pocket Pal

by Julie McGuffee

On a visit to the Outback, you're sure to see a Marsupial. These are animals that carry their young in a front pocket, or pouch. Kangaroos are just one example. This project is a fun way to remember this important attribute of a marsupial, while making a fabric purse for yourself.

You will need:
Foam - Brown and Black
2" Beige pom pom
1½" Beige pom pom
1" Brown pom pom
Three 1" Beige pom poms
Two ¾" Beige pom poms
¾" Dark Brown pom pom
Brown fake fur
Tacky glue
Scissors
Small hole punch
1 yard of ribbon or cord
Black marker

1. Cut a 3½" x 4½" rectangle from brown foam and a second rectangle from fake fur. Cut four paws from black foam. Note: It is easier to cut fur from the back.

2. Glue one paw to each corner of the brown foam. Cut a 1½" strip from the short edge of the fur rectangle then glue this at the top of the foam over the paws.

3. Glue the remaining piece of fur on the front of the foam piece along the edges only. This will form the "pocket".

4. To make the head, glue the large pom pom to the center of the strip of fur at the top. Holding the center of the larger dark brown pom pom between the finger and thumb of one hand, trim the pom pom on one side to flatten. (Do not cut through the center, or the pom pom will fall apart.) Glue to the center of the head for a nose. Trim two of the medium beige pom poms in the same manner then glue to each side of the head for ears.

5. Punch two circles from the black foam then glue to the head for eyes.

6. To make the "Joey" to put inside the pocket, glue pom poms together in the same manner. Use the medium pom pom for the head, the dark brown pom pom for the nose and the two tiny pom poms for the ears. Press the tip of a black marker into the pom pom above the nose to make eyes.

7. Cut four small paws from black foam then glue into body.

8. Glue ends of ribbon to the back of the foam at the top corners.

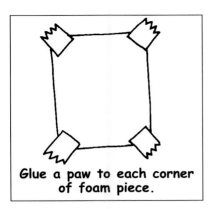

Glue a paw to each corner of foam piece.

GLUE POM POMS TOGETHER TO MAKE THE HEAD.

SMALL PAW PATTERN

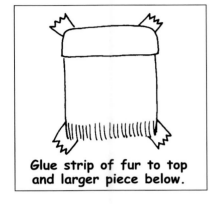

Glue strip of fur to top and larger piece below.

GLUE SMALLER POM POMS TOGETHER TO MAKE THE BABY KANGAROO (A JOEY).

LARGE PAW PATTERN

Glue ends of ribbon to back for strap.

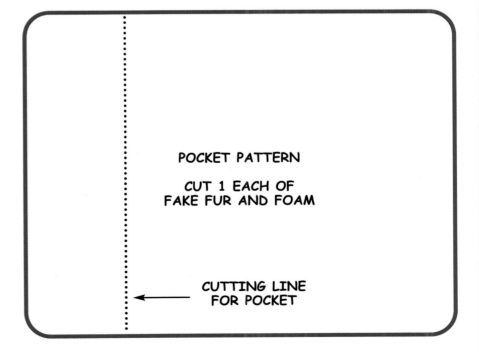

POCKET PATTERN

CUT 1 EACH OF FAKE FUR AND FOAM

CUTTING LINE FOR POCKET

Trim off part of pom pom to make a flat spot.

Darice® Pom Pom's, Fake Fur, Foamies™; Elmer's® Craft Bond™ Tacky Paste; Fiskars® Scissors, Hole Punch; Sakura of America Permapaque™ Opaque Paint Marker

Aboriginal Oil Pastels

by Judy Ball Johnson

Aborigine paintings were originally painted in the sand and only lasted until the wind blew. This art form employs a basic set of symbols, such as dots, concentric circles, curved and straight lines. All are based on the Aboriginal religion, the "Dreaming". Create your own oil pastel picture in this unique and ageless style.

You will need:
Construction paper - Black
Pencils and erasers
Oil pastels
Poster board - White
Glue

1. Using a pencil or chalk create a design on black paper using symbols of Australian art. Australian animals make a delightful subject matter in conjunction with the symbols. The drawing must be large so it will be easy to color in with the blunt oil pastels.

2. Fill in images with oil pastels. Some of the images need to be filled in solid and then outlined with dots like the Aboriginal Art. Dots should be placed around each major shape.

3. Leave some of the black spaces open for contrast.

4. Work until almost all areas of the construction paper are colored.

5. With some colors of oil pastels, white will need to be added for contrast.

6. Cut a piece of poster board 1" longer and 1" wider than your artwork, then glue the finished artwork to the center.

Color picture then center on a larger piece of tag or posterboard to frame.

Bemiss-Jason Spectra® Construction Paper and Poster Board;
Sakura of America Cray-Pas® Oil Pastels; Elmer's® Craft Bond™ Paper Craft Glue Gel.

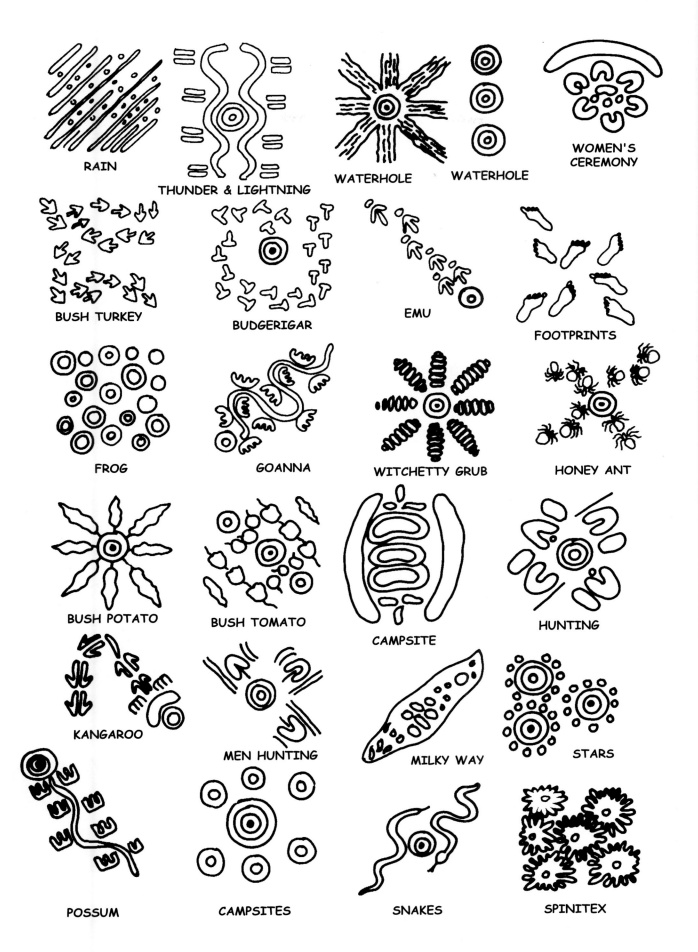

RAIN

THUNDER & LIGHTNING

WATERHOLE

WATERHOLE

WOMEN'S CEREMONY

BUSH TURKEY

BUDGERIGAR

EMU

FOOTPRINTS

FROG

GOANNA

WITCHETTY GRUB

HONEY ANT

BUSH POTATO

BUSH TOMATO

CAMPSITE

HUNTING

KANGAROO

MEN HUNTING

MILKY WAY

STARS

POSSUM

CAMPSITES

SNAKES

SPINITEX

Aboriginal Punched Bolo Tie

by Cindy Gorder

Punched paper dots are the paint for this original bolo tie. Learn some of the Aboriginal symbols such as concentric circles for campsites or waterholes; straight lines for routes between places; wavy lines for rain or water; "U" shapes for sitting people, and tracks for animal footprints. Also, animals are shown from above, plants are stylized and dotted backgrounds are traditional.

You will need:
Construction paper - Black
Waffle paper - Blue, Red, Tan
   and Yellow
Foam sheet - Black
Circle cutter
Hand punches:
   ¼" circle, ⅛" circle, ¼" rectangle,
   ³⁄₁₆" triangle, ³⁄₁₆" square, ⁵⁄₁₆" oval
   and ⁵⁄₁₆" diamond
24 Pony Beads
36" of Twine
Bolo tips and slide
Toothpick
Scissors
Glue

1. Use the circle cutter to cut a 4" circle from black construction paper or use scissors and a compass to draw a circle.

2. Using the paper circle as a pattern, cut another circle from the foam.

3. Use the punches to make lots of colored shapes from the waffle paper.

4. Apply glue to small areas of the paper circle then carefully apply punched shapes to make the mosaic. Start your mosaic with four yellow ovals to make the dog's feet, then work up the legs then the body and head. Fill in the ground and sky last. Dip the toothpick in a tiny amount of glue and use it as a tool to pick up a punched shape and position it on the mosaic.

5. When your mosaic is complete and the glue has dried, glue the paper circle to the foam circle. Weight with a couple of books until it dries.

6. Glue the bolo slide to the back of the circle then thread the twine through the slide.

7. Slide an equal number of beads onto the ends of the twine then knot the ends. Add metal tips over the knots at the end of the twine.

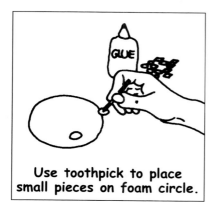

Use toothpick to place small pieces on foam circle.

Place pieces on foam to form the bolo pattern.

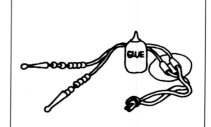

Thread twine through slide and pony beads, and caps onto ends of twine.

Fiskars® Scissors, Circle Cutter & Hand Punches; Bemiss-Jason Spectra® Construction & Waffle Paper; Darice® Hemp Twine, Pony Beads, Metal Bolo Tips & Slide and Foamies™; Elmer's® School Glue

Crocodile Candles

by Tracia Ledford Williams

Crocodiles are one of the most well known inhabitants of the Outback. Create and decorate a unique candle to light your way on a dark trek into the wilderness.

You will need:
Soap & candle paint - Purple, Yellow,
  Green and Orange
Soap & candle varnish
Acrylic paint - Green, Yellow and Orange
Paint brushes
Mini craft sticks
Tacky paste
Black permanent pen
Tuna can
Watercolor paper
Scissors
Pillar candle

1. Trace the crocodile pattern onto watercolor paper then cut out with scissors. Paint both sides with green acrylic paint. Add a little yellow to his back. Let dry. Outline the crocodile and draw an eye with the black pen.

2. Paint mini craft sticks with ivory acrylic paint. Let dry then glue sticks around the tuna can with tacky paste to create a fence.

3. Use a liner brush and green acrylic paint to paint grass around the fence. Dip the paintbrush handle into orange paint then use to add dots around the grass for flowers. Glue the crocodile to the fence.

5. Use the soap and candle paint to paint purple, yellow, bright green, and orange dashes, dots, triangles, and wavy lines for the Aboriginal design on the candle. Let the paint dry. Finish with a coat of soap and candle varnish.

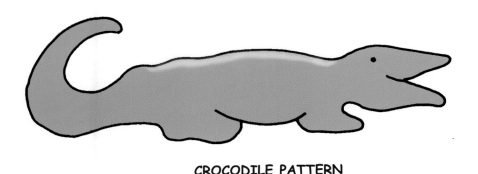

CROCODILE PATTERN

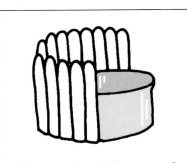

Glue craft sticks around
outside of can.

Delta Soap & Candle Medium, Soap & Candle Varnish, Ceramcoat® Acrylic Paint; Eagle® Kid's Are Painter's Too Paint Brushes; Elmer's® Craft Bond™ Tacky Paste; Forster® Mini Craft Sticks; Fiskars® Scissors; Bemiss-Jason Water Color Paper; Sakura of America IDenti-pen™

Woven Wall Hanging

by Cindy Gorder

Bamboo and rattan, (made from lianas or climbing vines) are some of the products of the rainforest. This project utilizes paper and paint to simulate the texture and design of a rattan wall hanging.

You will need:	Background rollers:
Tissue paper:	streamers, mesh
Green and Gold	and speckle
Colored paper: Tan,	Wide dye ink pads:
Green and Brown	Blue, Green,
Decorative scissors	Violet and Brown
Paper crimper	Scissors
Paper trimmer	Glue Stick
Heavy cardboard:	Twine
6" x 18" & 1" x 10"	Tape

1. Cut a piece of twine about 36". Make a knot approximately 12" from each end. Tape ends to heavy cardboard (outside of knots).

2. Fold both sheets of tissue paper in half then use the decorative edge scissors to cut several strips approximately 2" wide; separate colors. Fold tissue strips over the twine as follows: two gold, one green, and two more gold or a pattern of your choice. Run a strip of glue between the layers of tissue near the top to anchor them snugly to the twine.

3. Cut two 45" lengths of twine, and loop them around the base twine between the gold strips.

4. Use the ink pads and background rollers to apply all-over patterns to the tan, green, and brown sheets of colored paper (some of the ink colors will make very soft patterns).

5. Use the paper trimmer or scissors to cut several 1" x 12" strips from each of the papers. Run some through the crimper then glue together to make a longer strip.

6. Weave the 1" strips, plus a couple of additional lengths of twine, across the tissue and twine strips. Let the ends of these horizontal strips extend beyond the edges a little or a lot, as you like. Secure these horizontal strips to the vertical strips with a dab of glue as you go. This will keep the strips in place while you weave the next ones.

7. To finish, unravel the ends of the cords to make fringes. Trim the ends of the tissue and paper strips as desired with the decorative edge scissors.

8. Turn the cardboard over and glue a 1" x 10" strip of heavy cardboard along the top edge to reinforce. Tie loops for hanging to the ends of the top cord.

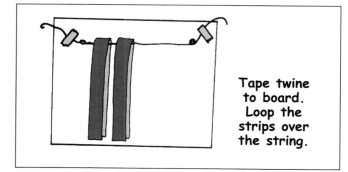

Tape twine to board. Loop the strips over the string.

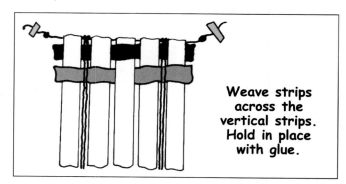

Weave strips across the vertical strips. Hold in place with glue.

Fiskars® Scissors, Paper Edgers, Personal Paper Trimmer, Paper Crimper, Brayer Background Rollers; Bemiss Jason Spectra® Luster Tissue Paper and Fadeless® Paper; Darice® Hemp Twine; Elmer's® Craft Bond™ Extra Strength Glue Stick

Leaf Print Floor Cloth

by Tracia Ledford Williams

Trees and plants of the rain forest have unique shapes and patterns. Use them to create an artistic floor cloth.

You will need:

36" x 24" piece of vinyl flooring	Masking tape
Acrylic paint: Light Green, Dark Green, Ivory, Bright Pink and Yellow	Sea sponge
	Wax paper
	Scissors
Exterior varnish	Paint brushes
Stencil sponge and holder	Terrycloth rag
Assorted leaves (real or artificial)	Toothbrush
	Pencil
	Ruler

1. With a large brush, paint the back of the vinyl piece with ivory paint. Let dry.

2. Apply a strip of masking tape 4" from the edge on each side of the rectangle.

3. Dip sea sponge into dark green paint then apply to outside border of rectangle. Dip same sponge into light green paint and apply over the dark green painted area, allowing some of the background to show through. Let paint dry then remove the masking tape.

4. Place leaves on wax paper. Attach stencil sponge to stencil holder then use to apply greens, yellow and orange paint to leaves. With the painted side down, press them to the center of the floor cloth to make a random leaf design.

5. Roll rag then dip end into bright pink paint. Apply to 4 corners of floor cloth where border and center area meet, creating flowers. Add some flowers around the leaves. Let paint dry.

6. Dip round brush into yellow paint then add a swirl to flowers. Dip paintbrush handle into bright pink paint and add dots around leaf prints. Do the same with yellow paint. Let dry.

7. Dip toothbrush into light green paint and spatter the floor cloth. Let all paint dry.

8. Paint a dark green wavy line around the edges of the green border with the liner brush.

9. Using a large brush, apply 3 coats of varnish, allowing each coat to dry between applications.

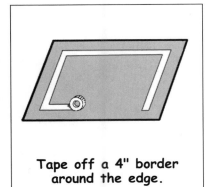

Tape off a 4" border around the edge.

Roll rag then dip into paint to paint flowers.

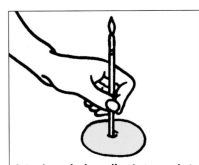

Dip brush handle into paint then use to paint dots.

Delta Ceramcoat® Acrylic Paint, Ceramcoat® Exterior/Interior Matte Varnish, Cherished Memories™ Stencil Buddy™; Eagle® Kid's Are Painter's Too Paint Brushes; Fiskars® Ruler, Scissors

Feathered Mask
by Judy Ball Johnson

Rainforest art reflects the environment and is usually functional. Masks play an important part because they are used in ceremonial rituals. They represent animals and spirits. Feathers have their own significance. This oil pastel mask evokes the colors and feather story of rainforest masks.

You will need:
Mask patterns
Poster board - White
Oil pastels
Construction paper
Feathers
Craft sticks
Pencils and erasers
Scissors
Glue
Paper towels

1. Trace mask pattern onto poster board with a pencil then cut out. To cut the eyes use a starter hole with a pencil. Cut carefully around the eye opening.

2. Using a pencil, lightly draw a symmetrical design on mask. Symmetry means both sides are exactly the same. (See example.)

3. Using 3 or 4 colors of oil pastels, color the mask in a symmetrical pattern. Blend colors for a feathery look. Work to completion, making sure to use a paper towel under the heel of your hands so not to smear the oil pastels.

4. Glue a craft stick at bottom of mask to make a handle.

5. Glue feathers to the back of the mask around the edge. Cut a small rectangular piece of construction paper then glue over the end of each feather to hold them in place.

Trace pattern onto posterboard.

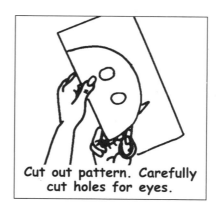

Cut out pattern. Carefully cut holes for eyes.

Glue feathers and a craft stick to back of mask.

Bemiss-Jason Poster Board and Rainbow® Construction Paper; Fiskars® Scissors; Sakura of America Cray-Pas® Junior Artist Oil Pastels; Darice® Feathers; Forster® Colored Craft Sticks; Elmer's® Craft Bond™ Paper Craft Glue Gel

MASK PATTERN

PLACE ON FOLD

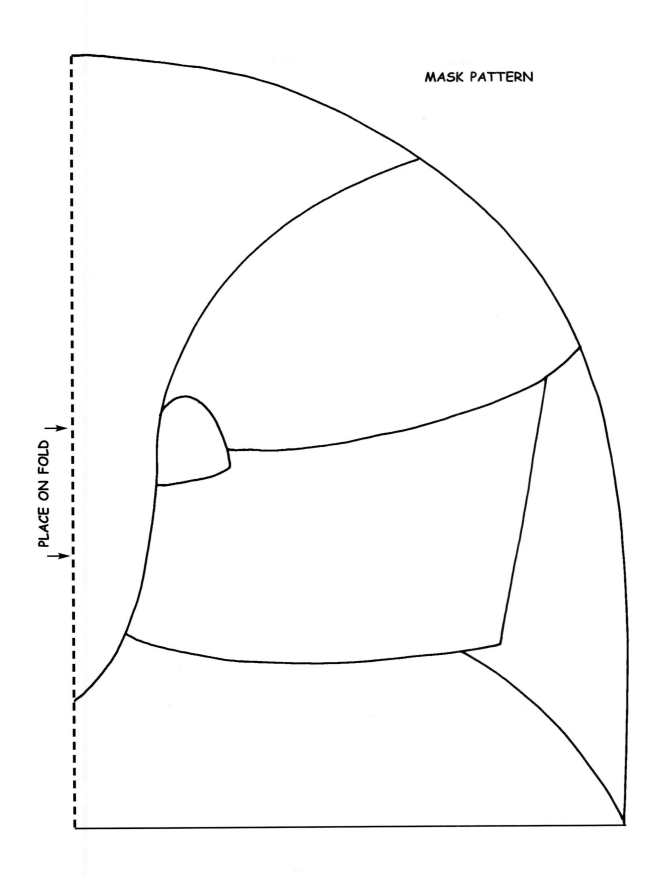

Toucan Candy Holder
by Patty Cox

All 37 species of Toucans are found living in the canopy layers of the rain forests of South America. Create this foam model of the Toco Toucan whose bill can be $7\frac{1}{2}$" long in the wild.

You will need:
Adhesive foam sheets: Black, White, Orange and Yellow
Tracing paper
2 Wiggle eyes (15mm)
2 Clear 8oz acrylic tumblers
Decorative edge scissors
Scissors
Glue
Pencil
Optional: Fruit candy

1. Trace pattern onto a sheet of tracing paper. Place pattern on foam sheets then cut out using scissors or decorative edge scissors for edges of feathers as shown on pattern pieces.

2. Peel backing paper from foam then wrap body piece around a tumbler. Overlap at the back. Add wings with scalloped edge toward front. Add yellow foam eyes then glue on wiggly eyes.

3. Peel the paper from top and bottom section of beak. Press pointed end together and use the wide end to adhere to tumbler for the beak.

4. For the breast feathers, peel the paper and layer as shown on pattern. Adhere to top of the second tumbler.

5. Peel the paper from the tail feather pieces and layer as shown. Adhere to the back of the tumbler.

7. Fill the second tumbler with candy then place the decorated tumbler on top to cover.

Option: Substitute glue and regular foam, or construction paper if desired.

Glue beak to front of covered tumbler.

Glue breast feathers to front of second tumbler.

Glue tail feathers to the back of the tumbler.

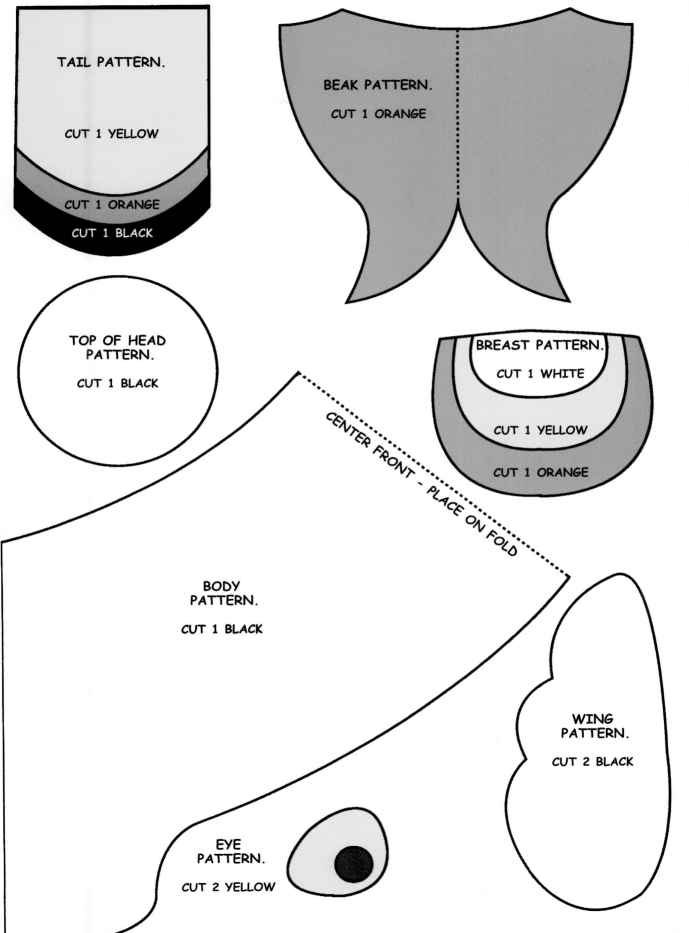

TAIL PATTERN.

CUT 1 YELLOW

CUT 1 ORANGE

CUT 1 BLACK

BEAK PATTERN.

CUT 1 ORANGE

TOP OF HEAD
PATTERN.

CUT 1 BLACK

BREAST PATTERN.

CUT 1 WHITE

CUT 1 YELLOW

CUT 1 ORANGE

CENTER FRONT - PLACE ON FOLD

BODY
PATTERN.

CUT 1 BLACK

WING
PATTERN.

CUT 2 BLACK

EYE
PATTERN.

CUT 2 YELLOW

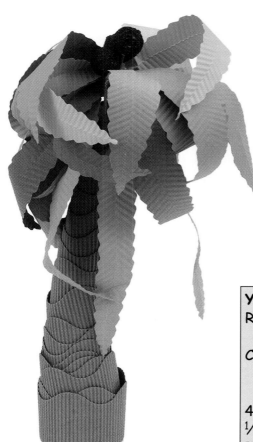

Palm Tree
by Cindy Gorder

Palms are one of the trees of the "Understory" layer of vegetation in the rainforest. This tree is totally made from paper with a surprise element; the coconuts are made from coffee grounds, another of the key products of the rainforest.

You will need:

Roll mini-flute border paper - natural	Decorative edge scissors
Construction paper:	Paper crimper
6 sheets assorted colors of green	Scissors
	Paint brush
4 Styrofoam 1" balls	4 Skewers
¼ cup fresh coffee grounds	Masking tape
Paper trimmer	Glue
	Optional: 3" Styrofoam cone

1. Separate the mini-flute border paper along the score line. Take one of the rolls, cut it in half then re-roll tightly.

2. Make the trunk first. Place your finger in the center of the remaining roll and carefully pull it up and out, making sure the layers of paper don't pull completely away from each other. Secure the center inside with a bit of tape. You can also use a styrofoam cone inside to stabilize. Continue to pull from the center, like a telescope, until the tree trunk is about 12" tall. It will hold together if you've made your initial roll tight enough. Glue the end in place then tape the entire length of the roll on the inside to prevent the telescope from retracting.

3. Next make the leaves. Use the paper trimmer to make 16 to 20 strips of green paper that are 7-8" long and 1½" to 2" wide.

4. Fold the paper strips in half lengthwise then cut a leaf shape from each one, leaving a 1" narrow stem at the base. Crimp each of the leaves while still folded in half.

5. Open up the leaves. Start with a 6" length of masking tape. Pinch the stem end of one leaf and wrap with one end of the tape. Add the rest of the leaves, one at a time, wrapping with the tape. Add new lengths of tape as needed. Keep the taped stems tight so they will fit into the opening in the trunk. When all leaves are assembled, add more tape, if necessary, to extend the stem assembly to 2" or 3".

6. To make the coconuts, insert a skewer or toothpick firmly into the center of each styrofoam ball. Use a paint brush to cover the entire surface of a ball with glue, While the glue is still wet, roll it in coffee grounds to cover. Set aside to dry (leave attached to the skewers).
Tip: Place the coffee grounds in a small plastic bag, or in a small plastic container.

7. Insert the stem end of the leaves into the trunk. Insert the skewers with coconuts into the trunk around the leaves; they will help hold the leaf assembly in place. Carefully bend, curl, and twist leaves into a pleasing arrangement.

Bemiss-Jason Mini-Flute Bordette®, Spectra® Construction Paper; Elmer's® School Glue; Fiskars® Paper Trimmer, Scissors, Paper Edgers, and Paper Crimper; Dow Styrofoam® Brand Plastic Foam; Darice® Craft Wire; Eagle® Paint Brush; Forster® Skewers, Dow Styrofoam® Brand Plastic Foam

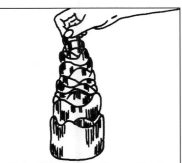

Carefully pull the rolled border up into a cone.

Secure the roll by taping on the inside.

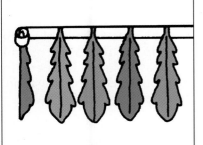

Glue leaves to tape, then roll up tightly.

Cover balls with glue then dip into coffee grounds.

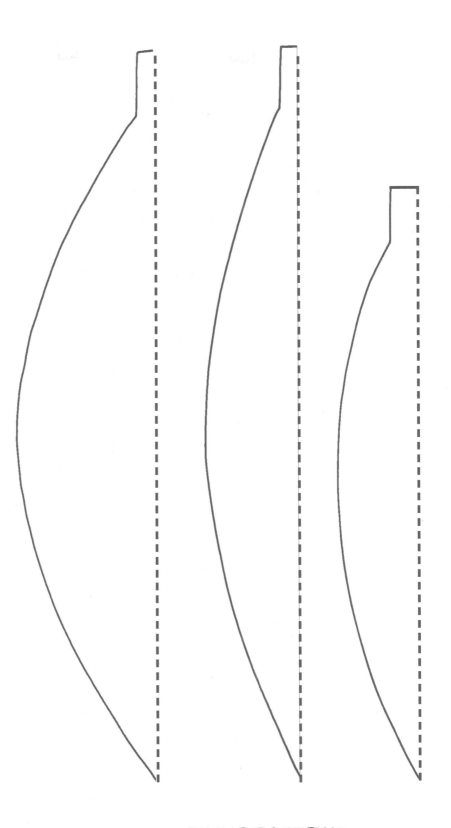

PALM LEAF PATTERNS

Endangered Animal Banner

by Carol Scheffler

Sorry to say, there are thousands of animals on the endangered list. Create a felt banner to remind you to help fight to "Protect Our Animal Friends".

You will need:
Felt scraps in assorted colors
18" x 18" Black felt
5 Strips of felt - 2" x 5"
¼ yard felt - Royal Blue and Green
5 Wood buttons
Thin tree branch, or dowel - about 20"
Scissors
Glue
Felt alphabet letters
Die-Cut machine and dies of various endangered creatures, or patterns:
 Rhino, Lion, Fox, Coyote,
 Moose, Koala, Penguin,
 Alligator, Hippo, Giraffe,
 Owl, Ape and Ostrich

1. Using the various colors of felt scraps, cut out the endangered animals with the die cut machine, or trace patterns onto felt then cut out. Arrange them in a circle on the large square of black felt. Cut duplicates of some animals in a lighter color to make a silhouette, or cut them apart to add details.

2. Cut a 7" circle from the blue felt then cut out shapes from the green felt that look approximately like the continents. (Look at a globe or map to help you.) Place them on the blue circle. Trim off any areas that extend over the circle's border. You have just created the planet Earth from felt.

3. Use the felt letters to spell out your slogan.

'PROTECT OUR ANIMAL FRIENDS'

4. When you are pleased with the placement of the felt Earth, animals and letters, glue everything down onto the large black square with the craft glue.

5. Glue the ends of the five strips evenly spaced along the top of the black square then glue the opposite end of the strip to the back of the square. You have just created loops to feed the stick through. Glue the buttons onto the front of each strip. Let the glue dry thoroughly.

6. Feed the stick through the felt loops then hang the banner in a place where everyone can enjoy it!

Glue strips to front of banner. Add buttons.

Glue opposite ends of strips to back to form loops.

Cut two animal patterns. Layer to make silhouette.

Darice® Wood Buttons, Felt; Fiskars® Scissors; Elmer's® Craft Bond™ Fabric & Paper Glue; Ellison® The Original Ellison® LetterMachine™, Decorative and Instructional Dies

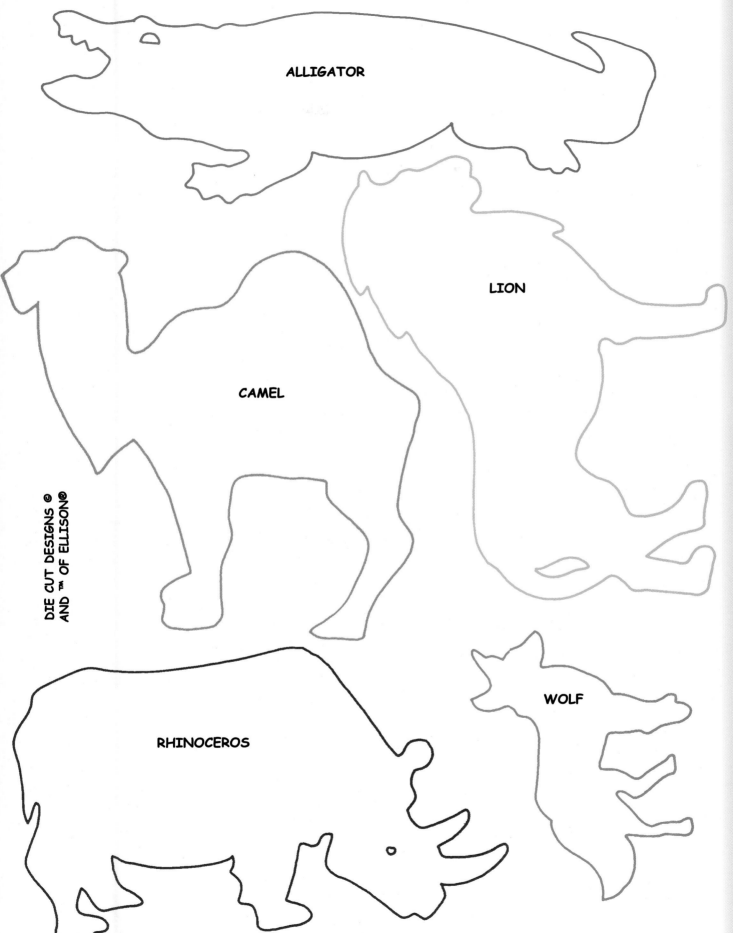

ALLIGATOR

LION

CAMEL

DIE CUT DESIGNS ©
AND ™ OF ELLISON®

RHINOCEROS

WOLF

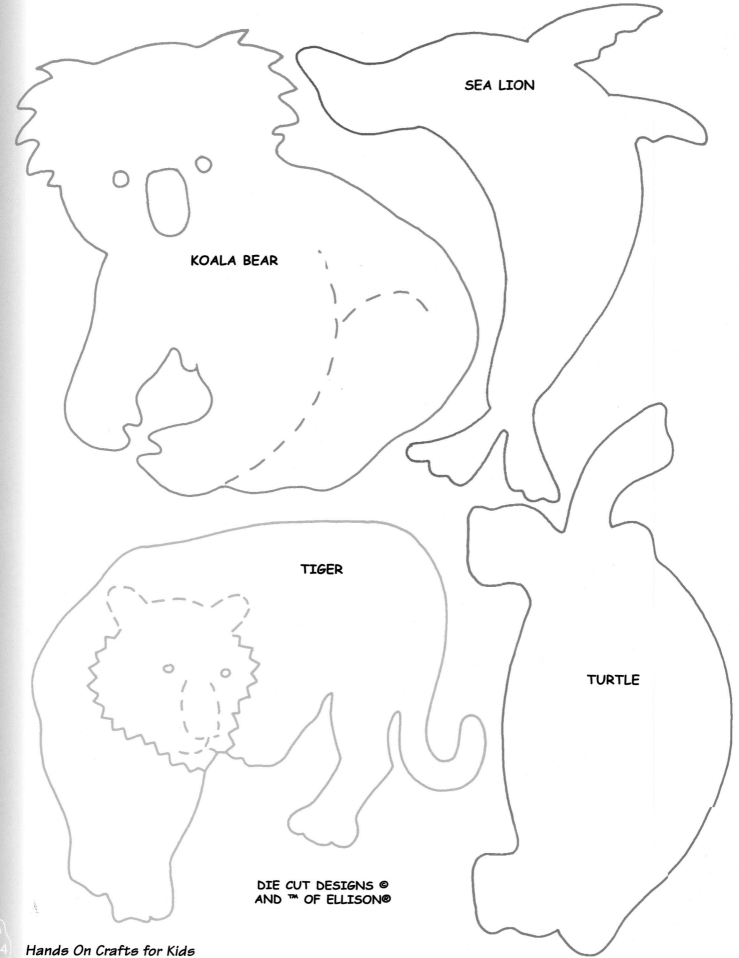

SEA LION

KOALA BEAR

TIGER

TURTLE

DIE CUT DESIGNS ©
AND ™ OF ELLISON®

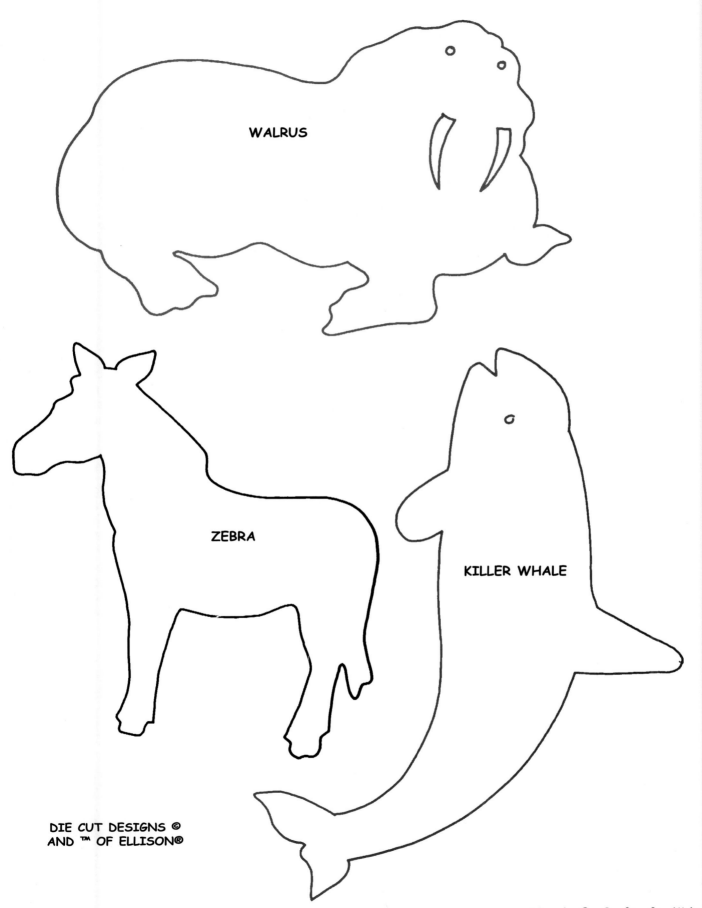

WALRUS

ZEBRA

KILLER WHALE

DIE CUT DESIGNS ©
AND ™ OF ELLISON®

Endangered Animal Flip Book
by Paula & Ken Moliver

Create your own paper book of different endangered animals. We researched and chose 10 for our book, like the whale, tortoise, sea otter, black rhino and walrus. You'll create a matching game in your book as you learn about these animals.

You will need:
2 contrasting colors of 12" x 18" textured paper
Construction paper 9" x 12" - Green, Blue, Turquoise, Sky Blue, Violet, Yellow, Orange, Red, Pink and Scarlet
Assorted colors of felt, foam and fabric (resembling animal skin)
Die-Cut Machine or scissors
Assorted dies or patterns of animals
Glue
Heavy thread
Large sewing needle

1. Make the cover first. Cut 2 pieces of textured paper, 6" x 9", for the front and back. Cut the second piece of textured paper into four 4½" x 2¼" rectangles and one 9" x 3" strip. Glue and wrap the rectangles around the bottom two corners of both front and back cover pieces.

2. Cut each piece of construction paper in half, so that each piece measures 6" x 9". Divide the paper into three, 3" segments. Mark with a pencil. Cut along the line up to 1" from the top.

3. Assemble the book by laying the 6" X 9" pieces of paper together. Align the top edges with the top edge of the back cover of the book. Place the front cover on top.

4. Use a straight stitch to sew the cover and construction papers together to make the book.

5. Using various types of fabric cut each animal shape using either a die-cut machine or scissors and patterns. Suggested materials: whale - blue felt; turtle - green foam; zebra and tiger - fake fur; sea otter and walrus - gray iron-on fabric; seal - navy suede; camel - cream suede; lion - gold iron-on fabric; rhino - brown suede.

6. Fill the first section of each page with interesting facts and information about one of the animals. Cut each animal shape in half. Glue the front part of each animal onto the second column of each page and the rear part of the animal onto the third section on a different page.
Note: Sections 1, 2 and 3 should not match. You will need to flip to each of the sections on different pages of your book to match the animal halves and your fact sheet.

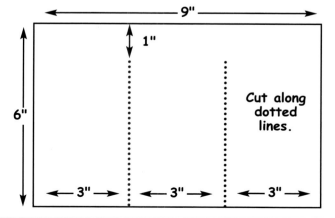

Cut along dotted lines.

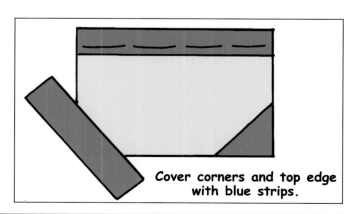

Cover corners and top edge with blue strips.

Bemiss-Jason Waffle Paper, Spectra® Construction Paper; Darice® Felt, Foamies™; Fiskars® Scissors, Elmer's Craft Bond™ Fabric & Paper Glue; Ellison®The Original Ellison® LetterMachine™, Decorative and Instructional Dies

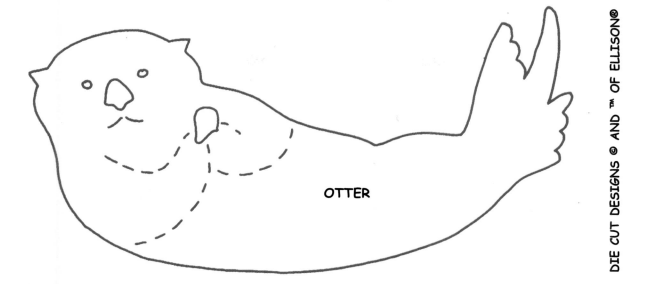

OTTER

Use the following information for the fact section of your book, or research your own.

Camel
Arabian camels have one hump and Asian camels have two humps. Even in the heat of summer they can survive several days without food or water. Since the 1920's, wild camels have been vanishing.

Seal
A marine animal with flippers that is prized and hunted for its smooth, sleek fur. Since it relies on trapped air in its fur for insulating warmth, oil spills kill many seals.

Turtle
Sea Turtles spend their lives in the open ocean. They are mostly in danger when they come ashore to lay their eggs. Egg poachers, meat hunters and shrimp nets still kill hundreds of these water reptiles each year. They are also hunted for their shells, which are made into jewelry, eyeglass frames and other items.

Whale
The Blue Whale is the largest and heaviest animal in existence. It can weigh more than 22 elephants. Once hundreds of thousands were swimming free in all the oceans. They (along with most other whales) have been hunted to near extinction. Today only about 1,000 big blues can be found in Antarctic waters.

Lion
A very large cat with a tufted tail and a loud roar. The males have a mane. Lions once roamed throughout southern Europe and in much of Africa and Asia but not in jungles. Mostly due to mankind's overpopulation and hunting in these areas, they can now only be found in Africa on savannahs south of the Sahara.

Rhino
A large thick-skinned animal known for its large horns. Unfortunately they have been hunted to almost extinction because of reported medicinal value of their ground up horn.

Tiger
The largest of all cats is known for its black stripes. All remaining varieties of tiger live in Asia. They are all near extinction due to the destruction of their environment, loss of their usual prey and being hunted, captured and poisoned. Only a few hundred of some varieties remain in protected preserves and parks.

Walrus
A large thick-skinned animal with huge tusks that lives in the frozen Arctic waters. They were overhunted for their strong skin, ivory tusks and blubber. Pollution has also killed many.

Zebra
Black and white striped animal found in South Africa. Their stripes actually serve as a camouflage and help to confuse predators. Dwindling habitats and skin hunters have dramatically reduced their numbers.

Otter
Sea Otters have sleek, furry, round bodies with webbed rear feet. They spend most of their lives in water and go to sleep wrapped in a blanket of seaweed. When they eat they use their belly as a table while floating on their backs. In the early 1900's trappers overhunted the otters for their fur, but since then they have become protected and their numbers are increasing.

Pull Toy

by Sandi Genovese

Learn about another group of endangered animals with a fun way to show some of their characteristics. Die cut paper is an easy and inexpensive base to our project.

You will need:

Die-cut machine or scissors
Dies: Bushel Basket, Colonial
   Pull Toy Tabs, Bananas and
   Gorilla
2 Metal round head ¾" brads
Green poster board

Construction paper: Yellow,
   Gold, Brown, Light Brown,
   Gray, Dark Gray, White and
   Black
Black Pen
Hole Punch

Glue stick
Tape
Pencil
Note: Cut shapes using patterns given when dies, or die cut machine are not available.

1. Die-cut toy tabs from green poster board.

2. Die-cut the bushel basket using two shades of brown. Cut an extra dark brown. Using the perforations as a guide, cut and layer the darker brown to trim the basket. Set extra dark brown basket aside.

Ellison® The Original Ellison® Letter Machine™, Decorative and Instructional Dies;
Bemiss Jason Poster Board, Spectra® Construction Paper; Sakura of America IDenti-pen™; Elmers®
Craft Bond™ Glue Stick; Fiskars® Paper Punch, Scissors

3. Die-cut bananas from two shades of yellow. Use the perforation as a guide to trim the banana from the peel. Attach trimmed banana to the peel using glue stick. Repeat with as many bananas as it takes to fill the bushel basket.

4. Attach bananas to basket through slit with tape, or glue. Glue the remaining darker brown basket to the back. Attach the completed bushel basket to pull tab bottom.

5. Die-cut two gorillas out of black and two out of gray paper. Have one face left and one face right. On the gray gorillas use a pencil to draw the trimmed areas. Cut and attach to the black gorillas. Repeat the same process for the gorilla facing the opposite direction. Add nose and mouth with black pen.

6. Line up pull toy tabs so that the holes are in a vertical line. Position the gorillas behind the pull tab holes and draw for position. Punch out the drawn holes. Attach the gorillas with brads to the front of the pull tabs.

7. Pull toys can be created with any number of endangered species, for example polar bears can be diving for fish. If the animal selected is too large to fit the standard pull toy tabs die-cut, create your own pull toy by cutting strips and circles and attach them together with brads. Embellish the animals and attach to the pull toy with brads.

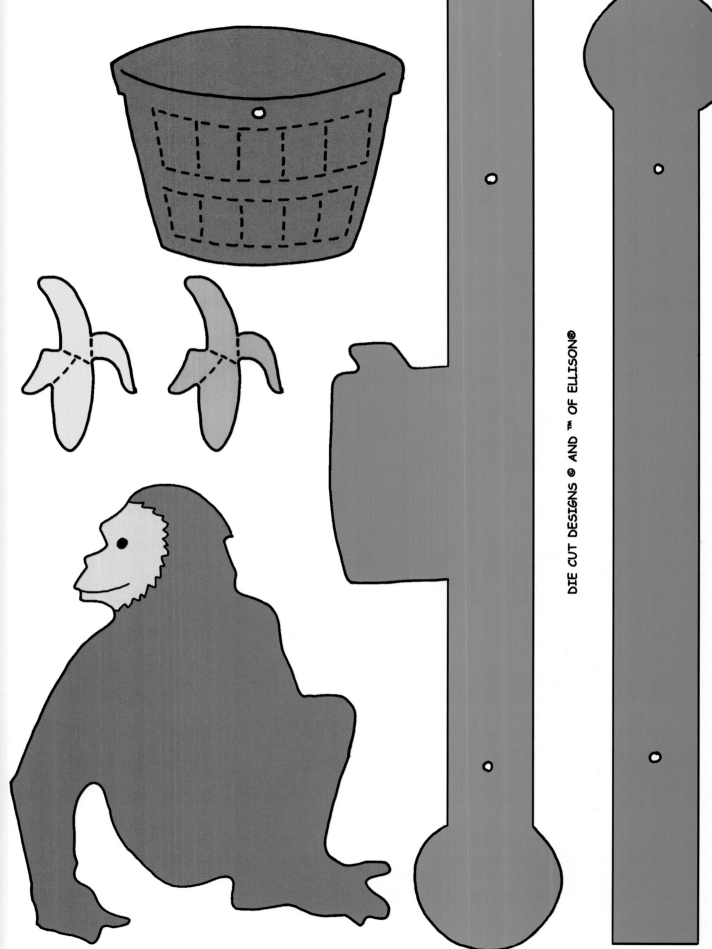

DIE CUT DESIGNS © AND ™ OF ELLISON®

Elephant Family
by Julie McGuffee

Both the African and Asian elephants are on the endangered animal list. This whimsical pompom and chenille mother and baby are from the Asian family of elephants characterized by smaller ears, hump shaped back and very short tusks.

You will need:
6mm Gray chenille stems
6mm Black chenille stem
White bumpy chenille
4 Spools 1" x ¾"
Gray paint
Paint brush
3" Styrofoam egg
2" Styrofoam ball

1. Wrap the styrofoam egg with gray chenille stems as follows: Starting at the center, push the end of the chenille stem into the styrofoam then wrap around the egg keeping the stems close together. Push the end of the stem into the styrofoam to secure. Repeat until most of the egg has been completely covered.
Note: The stems will not lay flat on the styrofoam at the ends of the egg. Wind one stem into a circle, bend the ends of the stem outward then push into the styrofoam to keep the circle in place. Use glue to secure.

2. Wrap the styrofoam ball in the same manner then glue the ball to the body. Use a toothpick to hold in place. Cut a 6" piece of chenille. Fold in half then twist together. Push the ends into the center of the head for the trunk. Make a small tail in the same manner.

3. Make two circles of chenille for ears. Push the ends of each circle into each side of the head for ears. Cut two white chenille "bumps" then push one into each side of the trunk for tusks. To make eyes, push end of black chenille stem into the head then cut off flush with the gray surface.

4. Cut four 2" pieces of chenille. Push into the bottom of the body where you would like the legs to be with about 1" of the stem still visible. Paint the spools gray. Let dry then glue one spool over each piece of chenille. Small elephants are made in the same manner using smaller spools and styrofoam pieces.

Cover styrofoam egg with chenille stems.

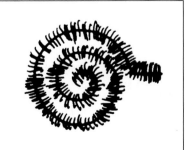
Roll chenille into circle to make ears. Push into head.

Push pieces of chenille into body. Glue spool over end.

Darice® Chenille stems, spools; Delta Ceramcoat® Acrylic Paint;
Eagle® Paint Brush; Dow Styrofoam® Brand Plastic Foam

Whooping Crane

by Julie McGuffee

This bird is perhaps the best-known endangered species in North America and, at about 5 feet tall, it's also the tallest. Snow white with black wing tips, it has a long neck, a dark and pointed beak and long thin legs. It is the only bird that flies with its neck straight out and legs trailing. You'll be making a wacky, walking or flying version of this beautiful bird from styrofoam.

You will need:
12" Giant white loopy chenille
6" Styrofoam egg
3" Styrofoam egg
2 Sheets of 8" x 10" white paper
White feathers
Black marker
2 Yellow beads
2 Black feathers
Oil pastel crayons - Red and Brown
Brown construction paper
2 stems Black chenille
Glue
Quilt pins

1. Accordion fold each sheet of white paper. Each fold should be about ¾" wide. Fold the folded paper in half lengthwise then glue edges together where the folds meet. Let dry then pull the folds outward to form a fan.

2. Glue a white feather into each fold at the outer edge of the paper. Let dry then turn the fanned paper over and glue a feather between each fold on the opposite side Place this second row of feathers so that most of the paper is covered. Color the tips of the outer row of feathers with a black marker.

3. Draw a stripe along the top of the small styrofoam egg from the point to the back with the brown oil pastel. Color the sides with red. Push a yellow bead into each side of the egg for eyes.

.4. Cut a 2" square of brown construction paper. Fold in half diagonally then cut along the fold line to make two triangles. Roll one triangle into a cone. Overlap, then glue the two ends of the triangle to form a beak. Glue the beak over the pointed end of the egg. Glue a small black feather to each side of the head if desired.

5. Cut a 12" piece of giant chenille. Push one end into the bottom of the head and the opposite end into the large styrofoam egg. Spread glue along the paper fold of the wing then attach one wing to each side of the body. Hold in place with quilt pins.

6. Push ends of black chenille stems into the body for legs. Fold opposite ends to make feet.

7. Unbend two paper clips. Insert the end of one into the body and the other into the top of the head. Tie a length of invisible thread to each "hook" and the opposite end to a coathanger.

Note: Use thin elastic cord instead of thread to give your bird some "bounce"

Dow Styrofoam® Brand Plastic Foam; Darice® Chenille Stems, Feathers and Beads; Sakura of America Cray-Pas® Oil Pastels & Solid Marker; Bemiss Jason Spectra® Construction Paper; Elmer's® School Glue

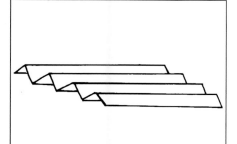

Accordion fold an 8½" x 10" piece of paper.

Fold accordion folded paper in half so that folds meet.

Glue feathers between folds of paper at the edge.

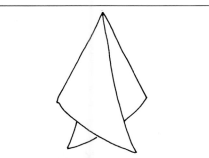

Fold triangle into cone shape for beak. Overlap ends. Glue.

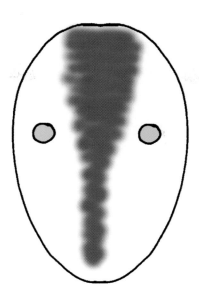

Draw a stripe along the top of the head. Press a yellow bead at side for eyes.

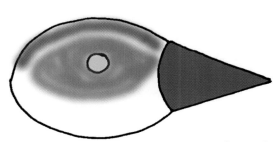

Color sides of head red around eye area. Glue beak onto pointed end of egg.

Bend end of black chenille stem into the shape of a foot. Insert opposite end into the body.

Unbend paper clips then insert into body and head to use as a hook.

Seed Greeting Card

by Patty Cox

Create a greeting card that will actually blossom into a bouquet of flowers. Make your own paper embedded with seeds and you can actually plant the card in soil, water it and watch it grow.

You will need:

10 mesh plastic canvas sheet
Acrylic paint
4 Sheets facial tissue
Seed packets and seeds
Colored paper - Purple and Green
Paper crimper
Decorative edge scissors
Scissors
White glue
Glue Stick
Spray bottle
Old dish towel
Rolling pin
Cookie sheet
Measuring spoons

Seed Paper

1. Place plastic canvas in sink. Lay a sheet of facial tissue on canvas.

2. Mix 2 tablespoons glue, 1 cup of water plus 1 tablespoon acrylic paint in a spray bottle. Shake well. Spray mixture on tissue, moistening the entire surface. Place another sheet of tissue over top. Spray surface with mixture. Sprinkle seeds on tissue. Place a third and a fourth sheet of tissue over top spraying each surface.

3. Place plastic canvas sheet with tissues on an old dish towel. Fold towel over the top of tissues. Roll rolling pin over towel to squeeze out excess moisture. Open towel then remove tissues from plastic canvas and place on towel. Fold towel over top of tissues. Roll rolling pin over top squeezing out more moisture.

4. Place tissues on a cookie sheet to dry. Tissues will dry quickly if placed outside on a sunny day, or baked in a warm oven for about 10 minutes.

6. Clean spray bottle, rolling pin, sink and plastic canvas with dish soap and water. Rinse out towel with warm water.

Greeting Card

1. Fold seed paper in half. Trim the edges with decorative edge scissors.

2. Cut out picture of flower, name of flower and planting instructions from the seed packet.

3. Tear a 3" square of colored paper. Glue square on card front with glue stick.

4. Fold small pieces of green paper in half. Tear two pointed oval shapes for leaves. Run folded leaves through the paper crimper at an angle. Open leaves. Glue leaves and flower on colored square. Glue flower name over square and the planting instructions on inside of card.

**Glue square of colored paper and picture from seed packet to front of card.
Crimp two ovals to make leaves.**

**Bemiss Jason Fadeless® Paper; Fiskars® Paper Crimper, Paper Edgers, Scissors;
Elmer's® White School Glue, Craft Bond™ Glue Stick;
Darice® Plastic Canvas;Delta Cherished Memories™ Acid-Free Paper Paint**

Flower Whirlygigs

by Julie McGuffee

Make a fanciful wooden windmill flower to decorate your backyard garden. The wind has a very important role in pollination of flowers and transporting seeds. Flowers and their beautiful appearance actually evolved to attract bees for pollination.

You will need:
Acrylic paint - Orange, Turquoise, Red, White and Green
18 Large wood teardrops
6 Wood 1" wheels
3 Flower stakes or dowels
6 Large wood hearts
Paint brush
24 gauge wire stems
Glue

1. Paint six wood teardrops for each flower the color of your choice. Paint both sides of the wood wheels yellow and the hearts green.

2. Let the paint dry then use the paint brush handle to add white dots to each flower petal.

3. Glue the pointed end of each of 6 teardrops to the flat side of one wheel around the hole in the center. Note: It is easier to arrange the wood teardrops in a circle on a flat surface then glue the wheel on top. Let dry, then glue a second wheel to the back of the teardrops aligning the holes in the wheels.

4. Cut a 6" piece of wire. Wrap one end tightly around the top of a painted dowel or flower stake. Thread the opposite end through the hole in the center of your flower. Curl the end of the wire by wrapping around a paint brush handle or dowel. The flower should spin freely on the wire.

5. Glue a heart to each end of a wire stem. Wrap around the flower stake for leaves. Glue a piece of paper over the wire for security. Let dry then paint over the paper.

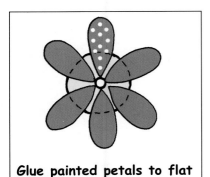

Glue painted petals to flat side of one wheel.

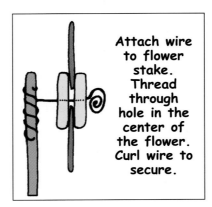

Attach wire to flower stake. Thread through hole in the center of the flower. Curl wire to secure.

Glue wire to back of heart. Secure with paper.

Delta Ceramcoat® Acrylic Paint; Forster® Dowels and Woodsies™; Eagle® Paint Brush; Elmer's® School Glue; Darice® Wire Stems and Wood Wheels

Bumble Bee Mobile

by Julie McGuffee

Take a buzz through the garden with a honey bee mobile. Did you know that bees can fly 22 miles per hour and their wings beat 180 beats per second? You'll really need to be "buzzing" to keep up with them. Bees unwittingly carry pollen on their back legs from flower to flower so that the plant can produce seeds for the next crop.

You will need:
4 Styrofoam 2" eggs
3" Styrofoam egg
24 Yellow 6mm chenille stems
18 Black 6mm chenille stems
Wiggle eyes
Black craft wire
Jute
16 Large wood teardrops
2 Small wood rectangles
White acrylic paint
Paint brush
Glue
Nylon thread
18 gauge Wire stem
Wire snips

1. Wrap each 2" styrofoam egg with yellow chenille stems. Starting at the widest part of the egg, push one end of a stem into the styrofoam then wrap the chenille tightly around the egg. Wrap black chenille between the yellow for stripes. To cover each end, form black chenille stem into a circle. Bend the ends outward then attach one circle to each end of the egg by pushing the ends into the body. Secure with glue.

2. Cut one chenille stem into 6 pieces. Push ends into the body then bend to make legs.

3. Paint the wood teardrops white. Let dry then push the pointed ends of four teardrops into each bee. To make antennae, cut a 6" piece of craft wire. Fold in half then twist together. Curl each end around a paintbrush handle. Fold in half then push into the head. Glue wiggle eyes in place.

4. Unbend four paperclips. Push one into the top of each bee for a hanger.

5. Unbend a paperclip then push into the pointed end of the large styrofoam egg. Tie end of jute to the clip. Cover part of the egg with glue, then wrap the egg completely with jute keeping strands close together. Paint the rectangles white. Let dry then write "**HOME SWEET HOME**" on one side with the black marker.

6. To assemble, cut the wire stem in half then tie the two pieces together at the center to make a cross. Curl each end to make a hook. Tie invisible thread to each bee then tie the opposite ends to the ends of the wire. Tie the beehive to the center of the crossed wires. Glue the rectangles together on either side of the thread with the lettering to the outside.

Wrap egg with yellow and black chenille stems.

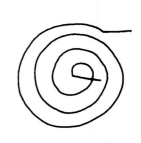

Form chenille into circle. Affix to ends of egg.

Darice® Chenille Stems, Wiggle Eyes, Craft Wire, Jute, Wire Stem; Delta Ceramcoat® Acrylic Paint; Dow Styrofoam® Brand Plastic Foam; Forster® Woodsies™; Elmer's® School Glue; Fiskars® Softouch® Craft Snips; Eagle® Paint Brush

Painted Watering Can
by Tracia Ledford Williams

You can't have a garden without water! Plants need this nourishment for growth. Create a fun design using special paint on a metal watering can.

Use finger to paint ladybug body red and head black.

Use liner brush to paint legs and antennae.

Dip paintbrush handle in paint. Use to make dots.

You will need:	White and Yellow
Galvanized watering can	Round paint brush
Metal paint - Red, Black,	Paper plate

1. Dip pointer finger into the red paint then use your finger to apply the lady bug bodies around the center of the watering can.

2. Dip baby finger into the black paint, apply the dot to make the lady bug's head next to the body. The lady bugs can go in any direction on the center of the watering can.

3. Using the round paint brush and black paint add the legs and the antennae to the lady bugs. Let the paint dry. Now dip the handle of the brush into black paint and apply the 6 spots to the lady bug.

4. Add large yellow dots using your pointer finger and yellow paint, around the top and the bottom of the watering can. Using the handle of the brush and white paint, add the small white dots around the yellow dots and trios of dots in the area of the lady bugs, creating the flowers. Add a black dot between each flower with the handle of the brush and black paint.

5. Add the following dots to the following areas, using the handle of the brush: red paint to handle, black paint to long part of spout and yellow paint to top of spout.

6. Allow paint to dry and cure for 10 days, then it is permanent.

Paint patterns around watering can.

Delta PermEnamel™ Paint; Eagle® Brush Kid's Are Painter's Too Paint Brushes

Clothespin Bugs

by Lynda Musante

Wire, beads and clothespins are all you need to create 3 examples of insects, the dragonfly, grasshopper and butterfly. The dragonfly actually spends most of its life underwater, but is actually one of the best flyers of the insect world. The dragonfly is a vital part of the ecosystem of a pond. While dragonflies are known to be beneficial, grasshoppers are known as pests and destroyers of crops. Lastly the butterfly is our most beautiful insect and common to the garden.

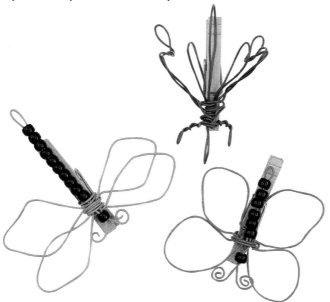

You will need:
3 Wooden clothespins
3 Colors 18 gauge wire - blue, green, red or other metallics
Black pony beads
Adhesive-back flexible magnet
Craft snips
Ruler
Scissors

Butterfly and Dragonfly

1. Use red wire for Butterfly and Blue wire for Dragonfly

2. Wings - Cut a 24" length of wire. Fold wire in half to find center. Fold each half in half. Bring second fold to center and twist into a loop. Bring loose end to center fold and twist into a loop. Repeat with other side.

3. Body - For Butterfly cut a 9" length of red wire. For Dragonfly cut a 12" length of blue wire. Fold the wire in half and thread on pony beads (6 pony beads for Butterfly and 10 pony beads for Dragonfly).

4. To assemble place body section onto clothespin. Position wings on body just over hinge area. Cut a 6" length of wire and wrap this wire around clothespin to hold wings and body in place. Cut off any excess wire. Shape wings.

5. Add one more bead to head and coil ends for antennae.

6. Cut a 2½" length of flexible magnet. Cut in half lengthwise. Peel off backing paper and adhere to bottom of clothespin.

Grasshopper

1. Back Legs - Cut an 18" length of green wire. Fold wire in half to find center. Bring one cut end to center. Twist folded wire together. Repeat for other side. Bend folded loops at right angles for back feet. Fold wire in half.

2. Body - Cut a 12" length of green wire. Bend wire into a right angle 3" from one end and twist into a loop. Bring loose end to twist and secure by twisting together.

3. Wings - Cut a 12" length of wire. Fold in half. Bring one loose end to center and twist into a loop. Repeat with other side. Fold wings back.

4. To assemble the Grasshopper cut a 12" length of wire. Fold back 2" from one end and twist to make front leg. Open clothespin and put this wire into small notch. Place body on top of clothespin. Put wings on body over small notch. Wrap 12" wire over these two pieces to secure. Put legs in place and wrap 12" wire around legs, body and wings to secure. Bring excess wire down and shape second front foot. Shape body, wings and back legs.

Forster® Spring Clothespins; Darice® Adhesive-Back Flexible Magnet, Pony Beads, Craft Wire; Fiskars® Ruler, Scissors, Softouch Craft Snip

IN THE GARDEN

Thread beads onto wire for body.

Attach to clothespin with wire.

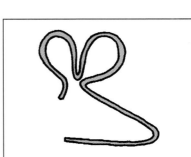

Bend wire in half then bend each half to form wings.

Twist loops and ends together at center.

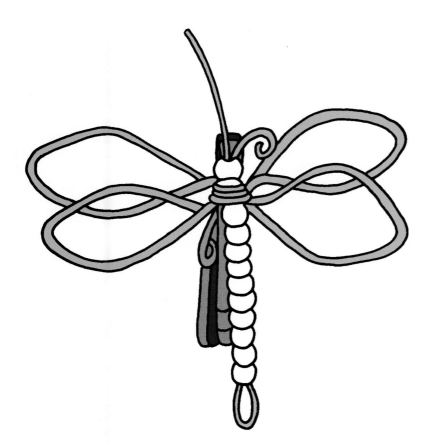

Attach wings, legs and body to clothespin with wire.

Desert Cactus
by Kathleen George

Cactus are found only in North American deserts. Styrofoam and toothpicks are the basis for this cactus model that needs even less water than the real thing.

You will need:

3" Styrofoam egg	3" Flowerpot
Styrofoam piece -	Sand
$3\frac{1}{4}$" x $3\frac{1}{4}$" x 1"	Marker
50 Round toothpicks	Plastic knife
Craft paint - green	Brown grocery bag
7" x 2" Tissue paper - Pink,	Chopstick or wooden skewer
Rose, or Yellow	Paint brush
6" Thin florist wire	Craft snips
	White craft glue

1. Cut off the tip of the narrow end of the egg. Divide into 6-8 equal vertical sections by wrapping rubber bands around the egg. Cut out V-shaped wedges about $\frac{1}{4}$" deep all along the marked lines. Use your fingers to pinch together the sides of the styrofoam wedges that remain. Remove any crumbs of styrofoam.

2. Use the craft snips to cut 1" off each end of 50 toothpicks. Note: Because the toothpicks can pop off in different directions when you cut, it's a good idea to snip toothpicks inside a large brown grocery bag.

3. Dip the blunt end of the toothpick into glue and then push it into cactus ridges in groups of 3 or 4 with the tips pointing away from each other. Allow to dry.

4. Paint the cactus and toothpicks green. Set aside to dry. Note: Push a craft stick into the bottom of the styrofoam to use as a handle while painting.

5. To prepare a pot for your cactus, cut a piece of styrofoam so it fits tightly into the flowerpot. Spread glue onto the surface then sprinkle with sand. Pat the sand down well with your fingers then glue the base of the cactus onto the sandy surface.

6. To make the flower, roll the strip of tissue paper into a tube along its short side. Wrap the center of the tube with wire. Twist the ends of the wires together. Cut slits into both ends of the tube of tissue. Fold the tube up and fluff out the cut ends to resemble flowers. Push the twisted wire into the top of the cactus with a dot of glue.

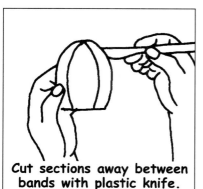

Cut sections away between bands with plastic knife.

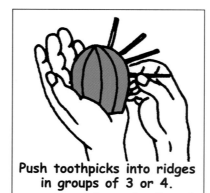

Push toothpicks into ridges in groups of 3 or 4.

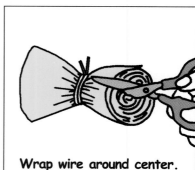

Wrap wire around center. Cut slits into ends of tube.

Dow Styrofoam® Brand Plastic Foam; Delta Ceramcoat® paint; Bemiss-Jason Spectra® Kolorfast® Tissue Paper; Darice® Florist Wire; Forster® Wood Skewers; Eagle Paint Brush; Fiskars® Softouch Craft Snip; Elmer's® School Glue

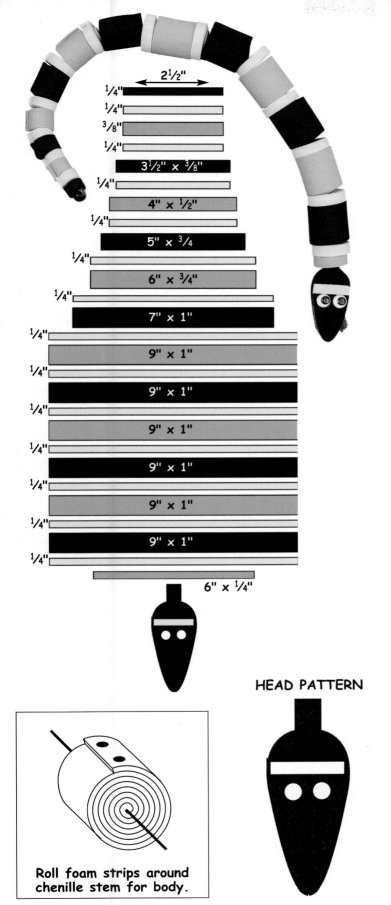

Coral Snake

by Patty Cox

The colorful coral snake is found in the southern desert region of the United States. It's small but very poisonous. Make his brightly colored rings with coiled strips of foam.

You will need:
Adhesive foam sheets - Black,
  Orange and Yellow
8mm Black bead
2 Red chenille stems
2 Wiggle eyes - 8mm
Scissors
Glue
Sequin pins
Optional: Plain foam sheets and glue

1. Bend a 1" hook in one end of two chenille stems. Interlock hooks then twist securely. Add a black bead to one end of chenille stem. Wrap a 1" hook around bead, then twist hook onto chenille stem. Trim chenille from stem around bead. Bend a 1" fork tongue at the other end of stems. Twist each fork together.

2. Cut adhesive foam strips as shown. Remove paper backing from shortest black foam strip. Beginning at bead end, wrap foam strip around chenille stem. Wrap the shortest yellow strip next to the black coil. Wrap the shortest orange strip next to the yellow coil. Push coils together toward bead end. Continue adding foam strips, graduating from the shortest to the longest strips. Insert a sequin pin at the end of each coil to hold in place.

3. Cut two head shapes with neck tab. Cut and remove paper backing on each tab on back of head only. Stick tabs and head backs together, on each side of chenille stem. Wrap the 6" orange neck strip around the chenille stem, covering tabs.

4. Cut a 1" x ¼" yellow foam stripe. Stick stripe across top of the head. Glue wiggle eyes below yellow stripe.

Roll foam strips around chenille stem for body.

HEAD PATTERN

Darice® Chenille Stems, Preadhesive Foamies™, Wiggle Eyes, Beads, Sequin Pins; Fiskars® Scissors; Elmer's® White School Glue

Gemstones
by Carol Scheffler

Gemstones might seem like an unlikely part of the desert, but actually much of the world's store of diamonds, silver, gold, bauxite, iron and copper is mined in desert regions. Use interesting paper shapes to create the facets of these gemstones.

You will need:
Die-cut machine, or patterns
Elastic
Geometric shape die cuts
Rubber bands
Black cardstock
Holographic cardstock - variety of colors
Gel pens - metallic colors
Gem stones
Glue
Scissors

1. Using either holographic cardstock or black cardstock and die-cuts, cut out the shapes needed to construct the mineral of your choice or trace the patterns onto paper and cut with scissors.

2. Fold up the wings on the die-cuts

3. Holding two pieces together, place a rubber band around the wings of the separate pieces. This will hold them in place until you are ready to glue them together.

4. Continue attaching pieces to your mineral in this manner until you are pleased with the shape.

5. Remove the rubber bands, one by one, and glue the wings together. Let the glue dry.

6. Decorate the mineral with the metallic gel pens. Use the craft glue to attach the gem stones. Let the glue dry thoroughly.

Secure glued edges with rubber bands until dry.

Decorate sides with glitter glue.

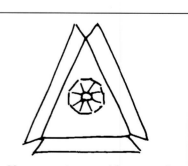

Glue sequins and/or acrylic stones on sides if desired.

Ellison® The Original Ellison LetterMachine™, Elastic Geometrics Set; Darice® Gemstones; Elmer's® Craft Bond™ Paper Craft Glue Gel; Sakura of America Gelly Roll™ Metallic Pens; Fiskars® Scissors

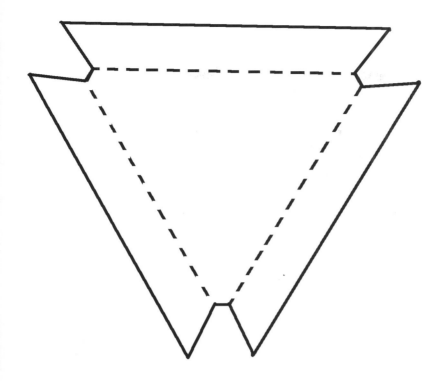

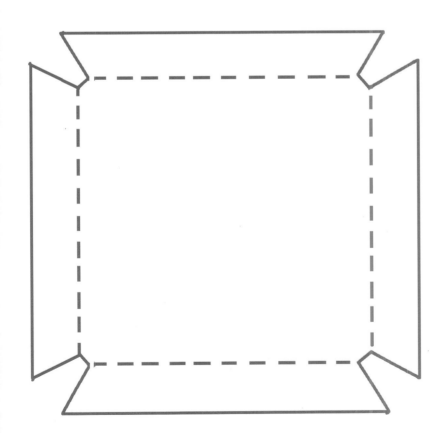

PATTERNS

Sand Painted Dunes

by Brenda Spitzer

When you think of the desert, sand is the first thing that comes to mind, but actually rocks are also a big part of the landscape. We use colored sand to create a desert landscape in the colors of the Southwest.

You will need:
Styrofoam block - 6" x 12" x 1"
Decorative gel glue
Glitter paint pens - Yellow, Blue,
   Red and Orange
Colored sand - Yellow, Orange, Brown,
   Blue and White
Acrylic paint - Brown
Corrugated paper - Brown
Tacky glue
Paint brush
Ruler
Pencil
Paper plate
Craft sticks
Straight pins
Scissors

1. Using a ruler and pencil, draw a line ½" from all edges of styrofoam block for the picture frame. Draw outlines of five sand dunes within the frame lines and a setting sun behind the sand dunes.

2. Squeeze decorative gel glue onto a paper plate. Sprinkle brown colored sand over gel glue and mix with a craft stick to make sand paint. Paint two dunes brown. Mix brown and orange sand with gel glue and paint two dunes with this color. Mix yellow and brown sand with gel glue and paint last dune with this color. Mix yellow sand with gel glue to paint the sun, and white and blue sand with gel glue to paint the sky. Paint the frame with light brown acrylic paint.

3. Use a red glitter paint pen to outline the brown dunes. Use an orange paint pen to outline the orange dunes. Use a yellow paint pen to outline the sun and the yellow/brown dune. Use a blue paint pen to outline the sky. Allow to dry.

4. Cut two 12-¼" x ⅞" and two 6" x ⅞" strips strips of brown corrugated paper. Use tacky glue to glue these strips in place over the side of the styrofoam. Use straight pins to hold paper in place until it dries.

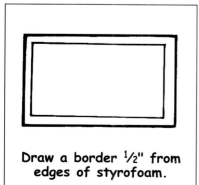

Draw a border ½" from edges of styrofoam.

Mix sand with gel glue on a paper plate.

Glue strips of corrugated paper around sides.

Dow Styrofoam® Brand Plastic Foam; Elmer's® Galactic Glue™,
3D Glitter Paint Pens, Craft Bond™ Fabric and Paper Glue; Delta Ceramcoat® Acrylic Paint;
Fiskars® Ruler, Scissors; Bemiss-Jason Mini Flute Corobuff®; Forster® Craft Sticks; Darice® Sand

SAND DUNES PATTERN

Center pattern on styrofoam sheet.

Lizard
by Cindy Gorder

Gila monsters, collared lizards and scorpions are some of the nocturnal animals common to the desert. Create a colorful, patterned paper lizard to brighten up the desert landscape. Gila monsters are not quite as colorful as our model, but they have a similar body type with a stout body, short legs and a short, fat tail.

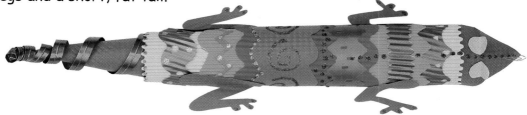

You will need:
Mini flute corrugated paper - Yellow and Orange
Waffle paper - Blue and Yellow
Construction paper - Purple and Lilac
Metallic paper -Blue, Green and Pink
Paper trimmer
Paper crimper
Decorative edge scissors

Hand punches - ¼" circle, ¼" rectangle, 3/16" triangle and 5/16" teardrop
26 Gauge craft wire - Light Blue
20" Paper twist - Metallic Blue
Glue
Tape
Scissors
Glitter glue

1. Cut paper into pieces as follows: 10" x 6" yellow mini flute corrugated paper, 8" x 6" orange mini flute corrugated paper, 6" x 6" purple construction paper, 3" x 6" blue waffle paper. Crimp purple paper. Trim all paper along widths with decorative edge scissors.

2. To decorate body, cut metallic and lilac construction paper into 8" x 2" strips. Crimp and edge with your choice of decorative scissors. Punch a variety designs with hand punches.

3. Roll the yellow mini-flute into a long tube and glue together (hold with tape on the inside) Decorate by gluing a colored strip around each end, keeping all seams aligned at what will become the underside of the lizard.

4. Roll the orange mini-flute around the center of the yellow tube, and glue to underside. Decorate the ends of the orange section with colored strips. Add the purple paper section next, decorate, and finally add the blue waffle section . Let the glue dry.

5. Tail: Roll a 4" square of blue waffle paper into a cone. Make the open end just large enough to fit inside the yellow tube. Tape the edges of the blue cone to hold the shape. Glue along the edge then let dry.

6. Use the pattern to cut head shape from blue waffle paper. Glue together then glue into end of yellow tube.

7. Glue tail into the other end, making sure to keep the seams of the head and body aligned on the underside.

8. When tail and head are secure, tightly wind a 20" paper twist around a pencil. Slide off, and pull the outside end to make a loop that will fit around the base of the tail. Slide the coil, which should taper to the diameter of the pencil at the narrow end, over the tail and glue in place

9. Make a small opening into the point of the mouth. Twist a flat spiral into the end of a 12" piece of light blue craft wire. Fold the straight end over 3", apply glue, and insert into the lizard's mouth.

10. Cut legs from blue waffle paper then glue to the body.

11. Cut two ovals from yellow waffle paper and glue to the head for eyes. Let glue dry.

12. Add pupils to the eyes, nails to the toes, and embellish the lizard with spirals and dots of glitter glue.

Fiskars® Scissors, Hand Punches, Paper Trimmer, Paper Crimper, Paper Edgers; Bemiss-Jason Mini-Flute Corobuff®, Waffle Paper, Spectra® Contemporary Fadeless® Paper, Metallic Fadeless® Paper, Art Fun™ Twists; Darice® Craft Wire; Elmer's® White School Glue, 3D Glitter Paint Pens

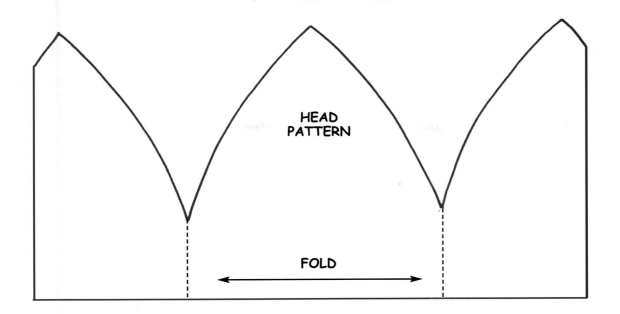

HEAD
PATTERN

FOLD

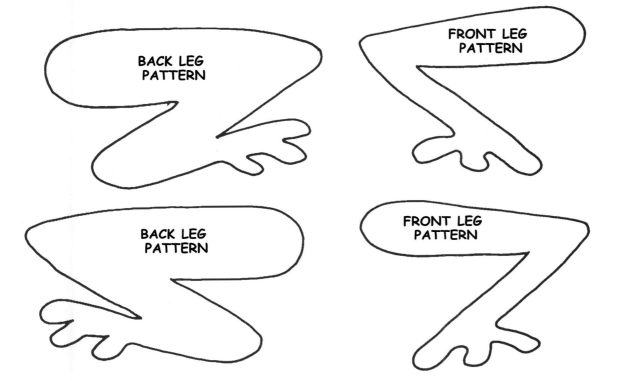

BACK LEG
PATTERN

FRONT LEG
PATTERN

BACK LEG
PATTERN

FRONT LEG
PATTERN

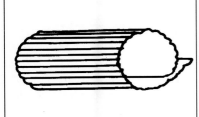

Roll corrugated paper to
form body.

Tape edges of cone on
inside to hold its shape.

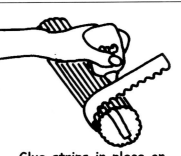

Glue strips in place on
underside to secure.

Scarecrow

by Tracia Ledford Williams

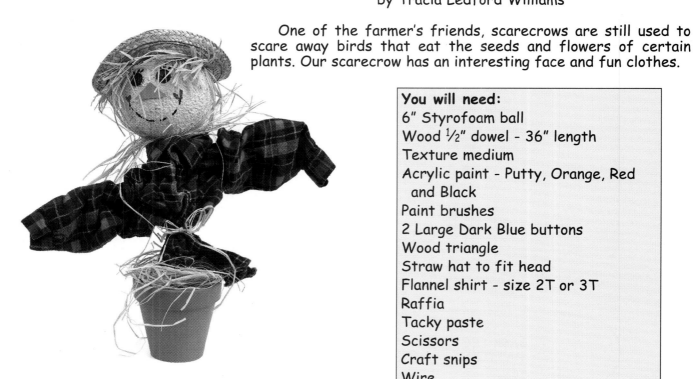

One of the farmer's friends, scarecrows are still used to scare away birds that eat the seeds and flowers of certain plants. Our scarecrow has an interesting face and fun clothes.

You will need:
6" Styrofoam ball
Wood ½" dowel - 36" length
Texture medium
Acrylic paint - Putty, Orange, Red and Black
Paint brushes
2 Large Dark Blue buttons
Wood triangle
Straw hat to fit head
Flannel shirt - size 2T or 3T
Raffia
Tacky paste
Scissors
Craft snips
Wire

1. Using the craft snips, cut the dowel in half. Take the two dowel pieces and wire them together at the center of each dowel to make a cross. Move one dowel up so it is 6" from the top of the other dowel.

2. Take the Styrofoam ball and cover it with texture using a brush. Let dry overnight. Paint the textured ball with putty colored paint.

3. Bend two, 4" pieces of wire into a "U" shape. Thread the ends through the holes in the buttons then push into the foam ball for eyes. Paint the wood triangle with orange paint. Let dry then glue in place for the nose. Using a liner brush and black paint, add the smile, then paint red hearts at each end of the smile.

4. To make the hair, cut raffia into 8" pieces. Tie 10 strands together with wire at the center, then push the wire ends into the foam ball, around the face. Glue hat on top of raffia hair.

5. Push the short end of the dowel into the bottom of the foam ball. Tie some pieces of raffia under the head.

6. Place shirt over horizontal dowel. Button up then glue to base of head, allowing some of the tied raffia to poke out of the top. Tie a piece of raffia around the waist of the shirt. If you are going to hang the scarecrow, add a piece of wire to the back of the hat for a hanger.

Attach bundles of raffia hair to head with wire.

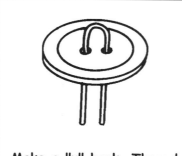

Make a "u" hook. Thread ends thru buttonholes.

Tie dowels together. Push styrofoam head onto top.

Elmer's® Craft Bond™ Tacky Paste; Dow Styrofoam® Brand Plastic Foam; Forster® Dowels & Woodsies™; Delta Ceramcoat® Acrylic Paint, Texture Medium; Eagle® Paint Brushes; Darice® Raffia, Wire, Straw Hat; Fiskars® Scissors, Softouch® Craft Snips

Aerial Farm Patterns
by Julie McGuffee

The view from above is one of the most fascinating views of a farm. Crops are planted in uniform rows that create interesting, geometric patterns. Use paper and pastels to make your own pattern.

You will need:
8" x 10" Tag or posterboard
Brown construction paper,
Green mini corrugated paper
Brown and Yellow Waffle paper.
Blue metallic Paper
Green tissue paper
6mm Green chenille stems
3mm White chenille stems
Paper crimper
Scissors
Tacky glue
Red glitter glue pen
Oil pastel crayons

1. Divide an 8" x 10" piece of tag or posterboard into various squares and rectangles. Cut a variety of papers into corresponding squares and rectangles then glue on the board. Each color should represent a different crop, or type of field. Use a paper crimper to crimp brown paper to look like a plowed field. Green mini corrugated paper could represent a field of grass and textured yellow paper would look like a field of sunflowers. Lightly color the top of the yellow paper with oil pastels for added texture.

2. Red rectangles look like the of a farmhouses and a barn and blue metallic paper would look like a small pond.

3. To make trees, crumple 2" squares of green tissue paper into balls then glue in rows for orchards. Add tiny dots of red glitter glue for apple trees.

4. Cut green chenille stems to glue between your fields for hedgerows and pieces of white chenille for fencing around the farm. You could even add small white dots on top of green "grass" to look like sheep grazing in the meadow. What other types of things do you see on a farm? Use your own imagination to create your picturesque farmland mosaic.

Crumple green tissue. Add red glitter dots for apples.

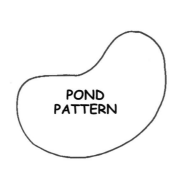

POND PATTERN

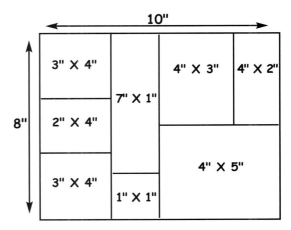

Bemiss Jason Spectra ® Construction Paper, Poster Board, Waffle Paper, Metallic Paper, Spectra® Tissue Paper, Corrugated Paper; Sakura of America Cray-Pas® Oil Pastels; Darice® Chenille Stems; Fiskars® Paper Crimper, Scissors; Elmer's® Craft Bond™ Tacky Paste, 3D Glitter Paint Pens

Farm Puppets
by Sandi Genovese

Cows, pigs, horses; these are some of the barnyard animals important to farm life. Make a cow puppet from a paper bag for fun.

You will need:
Die-cut machine or scissors and pattern
Dies - extra large puppet and cow
Construction paper - Pink, White, Black, Blue, Light Brown and Brown
Black marker
Brown paper bag - 5½" x 11"
Glue stick
Double stick tape

1. Die-cut the cow paper bag puppet out of two shades of brown, white and pink paper or use pattern and scissors.

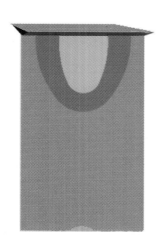

2. Take the pink tongue and light brown chin and fasten under the bag flap with glue stick.

3. Tape a swatch of blue paper behind the eye openings of the lighter brown cow. With a black pen, add the eye detail.

4. Tape a swatch of black paper behind the nostrils on the darker brown nose. Position the nose opening and tape in place on the back of the lighter brown cow face.

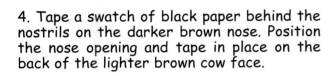

5. From the white cow trim horns and fasten onto the lighter brown cow. From the darker brown cow cut hair for the forehead and shading for the ears and fasten to the lighter brown cow face.

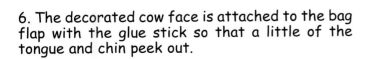

6. The decorated cow face is attached to the bag flap with the glue stick so that a little of the tongue and chin peek out.

DIE CUT DESIGNS © AND ™ OF ELLISON®

HEAD PATTERN

NOSE PATTERN

MOUTH
PATTERN

PLACE ON FOLD

DIE CUT DESIGNS © AND ™ OF ELLISON®

Hands On Crafts for Kids

Piggy Bank

by Sarah Stull

Farms aren't complete without pigs, notorious for being a very messy animal. Our pig is actually very clean and a perfect bank for storing loose change.

You will need:
Glass mayonnaise or pickle jar with lid -
  (about 7" high and 3" diameter)
4 Wood 1" spools
3" Spool
2 Large 1" wiggle eyes
Tissue paper - Pink and Purple
Decorative edge scissors
Pink fat chenille stem
Foam sheet - Pink
Acrylic paint - Pink
Black marker
White glue
Paintbrush

1. Paint the 5 spools and jar lid pink. Set aside to dry.

2. Cut tissue paper into 1" squares with decorative edge scissors. Apply slightly watered down glue to the surface of the jar. Glue on squares of tissue paper, overlapping to cover the entire jar up to the threads on the neck where the lid screws on. Apply a thin layer of glue over the top as a finish and let dry.

3. Glue large spool to the lid and screw to jar. Draw 2 black dots on the front for the snout.

4. Glue spools on the bottom as shown for legs. You will need a thick layer of glue to secure. Let dry overnight.

5. Cut 2 ears from pattern on pink foam then glue to top of the jar. Glue on eyes.

6. Curl the chenille stem around a pencil then glue to back of pig. Glue one coil to jar to attach firmly.

EAR PATTERN

Glue tissue paper squares all over glass jar surface.

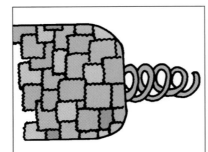

Curl chenille then glue to bottom of jar for tail.

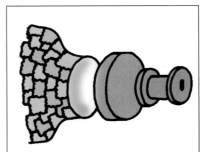

Paint large spool then glue to jar lid for snout.

Darice® Wiggle Eyes, Chenille Stem, Wood Spools, Foamies™; Fiskars® Paper Edgers; Bemiss-Jason Spectra® Art Tissue; Elmer's® White School Glue; Eagle® Paint Brush; Delta Ceramcoat® Acrylic Paint; Sakura of America Permapaque™ Opaque Paint Marker

Hauling Beans!

by Patty Cox

Watch bean seeds germinate before your eyes. In just 1-2 days you can see the bean sprout. The root starts down in search of food, while the plumule, or the embryo leaves shoot upward in search of sunshine.

You will need:

Die-cut machine or scissors
Dies or patterns - Tractor
Adhesive foam sheets - Red, Orange and Yellow
Black foam
Glue
Magnetic sheet
Adhesive back magnetic sheet

Cassette tape holder
Compressed sponge, or kitchen sponge
Bean seeds
Jumbo craft punch - star
Hole punch
Decorative edge scissors
Pencil
Rubberband

Bean Seeds and Wagon

1. To speed germination, soak bean seeds in a cup of water for three hours.

2. Cut sponge into a 2½" x 4" rectangle. Open cassette tape holder. Run pencil over post points. Place sponge in cassette holder then close the case. The graphite from the pencil will mark the placement of posts. Punch a hole in sponge at each post. Dampen sponge, (moist, but not dripping) then place sponge and bean seeds in the cassette holder.

3. Cut adhesive back magnetic sheet into a 2½" x 4" rectangle. Remove paper backing. Adhere magnetic sheet to cassette tape holder back. Wrap a small rubberband around center of cassette holder .

4. Cut and layer wagon wheels according to pattern. Use jumbo star punch or pattern and scissors to cut small designs. Cut paper backing from the top third of each wheel. Remove top paper backing only. Adhere wheels to the front of the wagon.

Tractor

1. Adhere a red sheet of adhesive back foam to magnetic sheet.

2. Cut the tractor shape from foam and the magnetic sheet with the die cut machine or use pattern and cut with scissors. Cut together, or cut one at a time then stick together.

3. Cut wheels according to pattern. Use decorative edge scissors to cut large tractor wheel. Remove paper backing from each adhesive back foam piece. Stick in position on tractor.

4. Stick tractor and wagon on refrigerator door and watch the bean seeds germinate!

Note: If pre-adhesive foam sheets are not available, use regular foam sheets and glue.

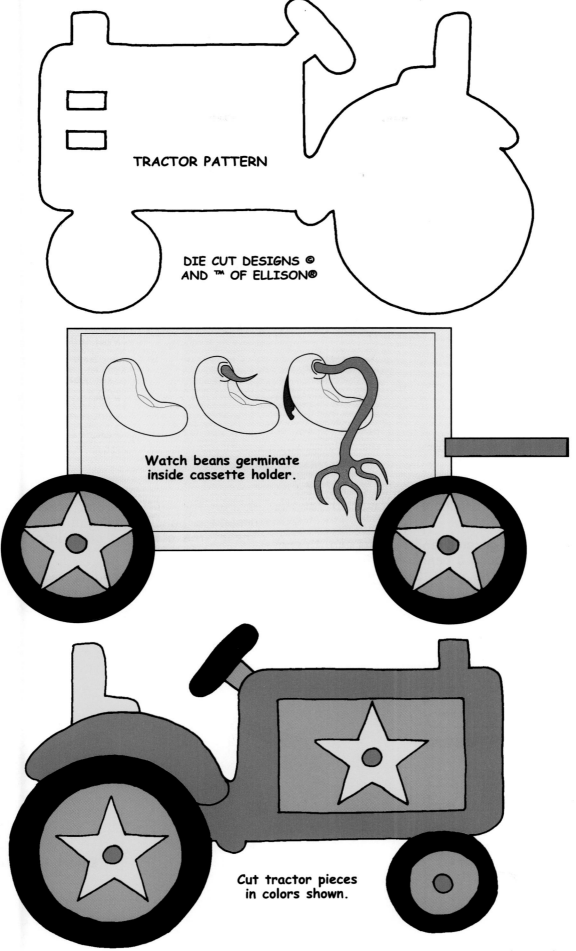

TRACTOR PATTERN

DIE CUT DESIGNS © AND ™ OF ELLISON®

Watch beans germinate inside cassette holder.

Cut tractor pieces in colors shown.

Dinosaur Pipe Cleaner Project
by Family Fun

Create your own dinosaurs with pipe cleaners, or chenille and pencils for some prehistoric fun!

You will need:
8 Chenille stems - Green
  or Yellow
2 Wiggly eyes
Large marker
Pencil
Glue

1. Connect three green chenille stems end to end. Bundle them around a thick marker for the body.

2. Connect two green chenille stems end to end. Bundle half around a pencil for the head, then coil some for the neck. Leave a 1" attaching stem.

3. Attach the head and neck by inserting the stem into the body (use glue, if desired for extra holding power).

4. For the tail, coil one green chenille stem around a pencil, leaving a 1" attaching stem. Insert the attaching stem into the bundle of the body.

5. Make legs by bending two green chenille stems into V's, then coiling each end around a pencil insert the legs into the body, between the coils. Glue if desired.

6. Glue wiggly eyes onto head.

Wrap chenille stems around pencil and markers.

Twist ends of chenille around pencil for legs.

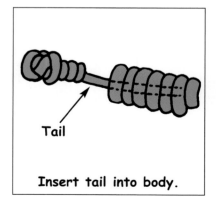

Tail

Insert tail into body.

Darice® Chenille Stems, Wiggly Eyes; Elmer's® White School Glue

Fossil Necklace

by Paula and Ken Moliver

Fossils are the marks left when plants and animals die and leave their imprint on the ground which then hardens into rock. You can also create your own fossil from clay and use it to string on an interesting necklace.

You will need:
Air dry craft clay
36 White fossil stone beads
5 Hairpipe beads - 2" black horn
4 Hairpipe beads - 2" buffalo bone
Acrylic paint - Dark Gray
Sparkle glaze
Shell or bone
Flat brush
2 feet mylar filament or dental floss
Toothpick

1. Roll the clay into a ball twice the size of the shell or bone you've chosen to use. Impress shell or bone into clay. Remove item. Insert toothpick through the side of the top and exit through the other side. Let dry.

2. Paint the clay with one coat of dark gray paint. Let dry. Paint the clay with one coat of sparkle glaze. The sparkles give the appearance of Mica, a mineral found in rocks.

3. Thread the filament through the fossil. Using the fossil stone beads make, a symmetrical pattern on either side of the fossil. Add the hairpipe in a black and white pattern. Knot the ends together. Hide the knot under one of the hairpipe beads.

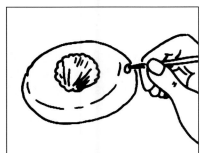

Impress shell into clay.
Make a hole with toothpick.

Let clay dry then paint
with sparkle glaze.

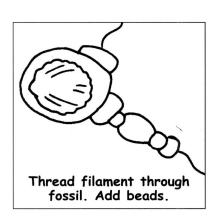

Thread filament through
fossil. Add beads.

Darice® Fossil Stone Beads, Hairpipe Beads, Mylar Filament; Delta Ceramcoat® Acrylic Paint, Sparkle Glaze™; Eagle® Paint Brush; Creative PaperClay®

Wooly Mammoth

by Kathleen George

The modern day elephant is actually a descendant of the wooly mammoth, that roamed the earth in prehistoric times. You'll love this furry creature that definitely looks cuter in our miniature size and a lot less ferocious than his real-life counterpart.

You will need:
Styrofoam egg $3^3/_{16}$" x $2^3/_{16}$"
Styrofoam egg $2^1/_2$" x $1^7/_8$"
Four dowels $2^3/_4$" x $^1/_2$"
Fake fur 12" x 15"
$3^1/_2$" Square piece of batting
Brown felt
2 White chenille stems
2 Black beads
Straight pins
Plastic knife
White paste Glue
Scissors
Craft snips

1. Round the pointed end of the large egg by rolling against a countertop.

2. Slice off a bit of the side of the smaller styrofoam egg. Twist the flattened area against the topside of the wide end of the larger egg until it fits snuggly. Glue the eggs together.

3. Gently insert the four dowel legs into the bottom of the large egg. Begin the hole with a pencil point. Push the hind legs in deeper than the front legs so that the egg tilts down slightly. Glue the dowels in place.

4. Fold the batting in half and pin on behind the head to create a bit of a hump.

5. Cut out the head/trunk and body pieces from the fur. Before cutting be sure to check that you have the fur pointing <u>down the trunk</u> on the head/trunk piece and pointing <u>towards the back</u> for the body piece. Cut out the four leg pieces from the scraps of fur. The fur should point <u>down on the legs.</u>

6. Wrap the leg fur around each dowel and glue in place towards the inside of the leg.

7. Fold the head/trunk fur piece in half and glue together $2^1/_2$" from the end of the trunk down to the tip. This will form the tube of the trunk.

8. Put a dot of glue on the top of the styrofoam head. Center the head/trunk fur piece over the glue and wrap the piece down and under the chin. Pin the fur tightly in place.

9. Fold the trunk down over the head so that the excess fur sticks out on either side of the trunk. Glue and pin in place. If the trunk seems a bit too long, trim to the correct length.

10. Place a line of glue down the center of the back. Center the body fur over the back and bring down tightly against the sides and pin and glue under the chin. Glue and pin the fur against the bottom of the body between the legs.

11. Wrap the two sides of fur tightly around the back. They will overlap. Glue and pin in place. Glue and pin the top flap of fur down and over the back of the mammoth.

12. Cut 2" off each chenille stem. Fold chenille in half and twist tightly together. Push the ends of the chenille up through the folds at either side of the trunk until firmly pushed into the styrofoam for the tusks. Secure with glue.

13. Cut out ears from brown felt. Glue ears to the sides of the head.

14. Glue on black beads for eyes.

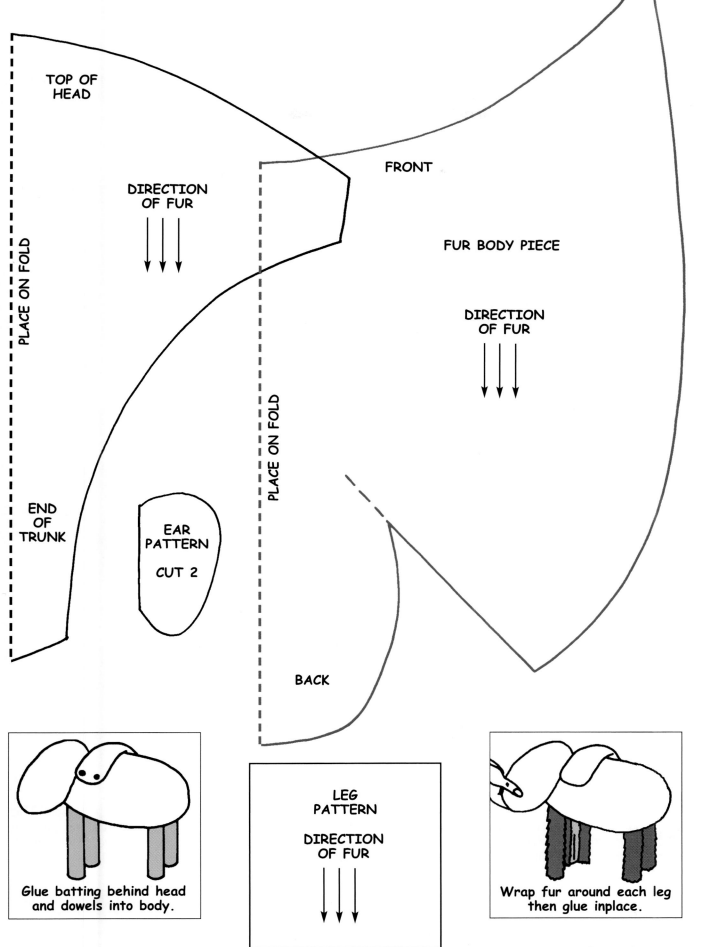

TOP OF
HEAD

DIRECTION
OF FUR

FRONT

FUR BODY PIECE

DIRECTION
OF FUR

PLACE ON FOLD

PLACE ON FOLD

END
OF
TRUNK

EAR
PATTERN

CUT 2

BACK

Glue batting behind head
and dowels into body.

LEG
PATTERN

DIRECTION
OF FUR

Wrap fur around each leg
then glue inplace.

Hands On Crafts for Kids

Dinosaur Dioramas

by Sandi Genovese

Brontosaurus, T-Rex, Triceratops, they're all here as a paper diorama. Now do your research and actually determine which dinosaurs existed at the same times so that your box is an accurate portrayal of prehistoric times.

You will need:
Die-cut machine or scissors
Dies or patterns - Diorama, Parasaurolophus,
  Pterodactyl and Stegosaurus
Construction paper - 3 shades of Green,
  2 shades of Yellow, Purple, Brown, Tan,
  Orange, Hot Pink, Blue, Black, Light Gray
  and Dark Gray
Craft punch - sun
Circle hole punch - $\frac{1}{16}$" and $\frac{1}{8}$"
Colored pens - Red and Black
Glue stick
Stapler

1. Die-cut the front with the palm trees out of green or use pattern and scissors. Cut a middle strip 9" x 1" out of purple paper and a 10½" x 4" rectangle out of blue paper for the back.

2. Die-cut the Stegosaurus out of pink, green and purple. The green color is the base shape. The pink and purple are the detail to layer with the green. Trim the purple armored plates and glue on the green Stegosaurus. Trim the first three armored plates off of the pink and glue on the back so that they show through. Use black pen to draw the eye and add texture to the skin

Ellison® The Original Ellison® LetterMachine™, Decorative and Instructional Dies;
Bemiss Jason Spectra® Construction Paper; Sakura of America IDenti-pen™;
Fiskars® Scissors, Paper Punch; Elmer's® Craft Bond™ Glue Stick

PATTERN

3. Use the same techniques to embellish the Parasaurolophus by layering the light gray shape which is hole punched onto the dark gray base shape. The head crest is die-cut from yellow with the tip colored with the red pen. Glue the dinosaurs to the middle strip.

4. Embellish the Pterodactyl by hole punching the top layer of tan to allow the darker brown to show through. Using a glue stick attach the tan bill and create the eye with a black pen.

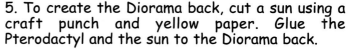

PATTERN

5. To create the Diorama back, cut a sun using a craft punch and yellow paper. Glue the Pterodactyl and the sun to the Diorama back.

6. Line up the Diorama front, middle and back and staple on the left side top and bottom. Line up the edges on the right side then staple to create the three dimensional effect.

7. Once you cut the front, middle and back pieces out of multiple colors for the Diorama and the dinosaurs, it is a simple task to embellish the palm trees on the front, the dinosaurs in the middle and the moon on the back.

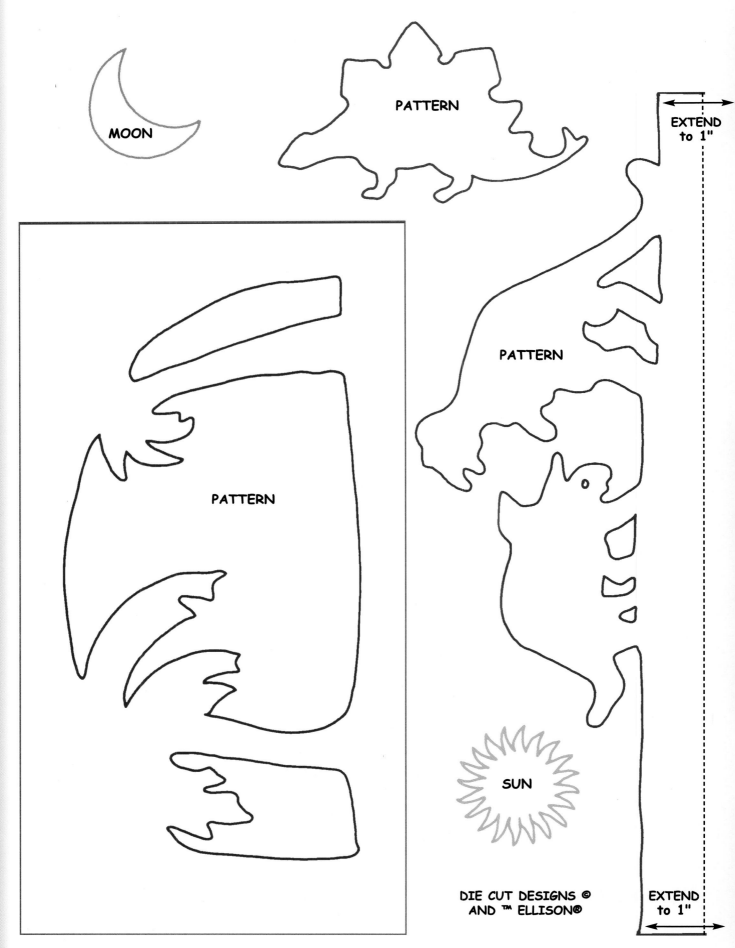

MOON

PATTERN

EXTEND
to 1"

PATTERN

PATTERN

SUN

EXTEND
to 1"

DIE CUT DESIGNS ©
AND ™ ELLISON®

Dinosaur Soaps

by Tracia Ledford Williams

It's hard to resist adding a fun project to clean up. Make decorative soaps for a fun look at dinosaurs.

Place soap cubes in microwave safe container.

Place plastic animals into mold before adding soap.

Pour liquid soap into mold. Allow to harden.

Twist mold to remove piece of soap.

You will need:
Clear glycerin soap
Colored glycerin soap
Soap molds
Plastic dinosaurs
Microwave
Glass measuring cups
Sharp knife
Optional: glitter and fragrance oil

1. Have an adult, cut clear glycerin soap into 1" cubes and colored glycerin soap into ¼" cubes. Place into glass measuring cups and heat in the microwave on high for 15 seconds at a time. Check between times. Do not overheat soap, just melt it.

2. Place dinosaurs into the molds, pour clear glycerin over them, and place small colored pieces of glycerin into the mold around the dinosaur.

3. Allow soap to cool 1-2 hours, or place into refrigerator for 30 minutes. Lightly twist mold and remove soaps from mold.

4. Soaps can be placed in a clear cellophane bag and decorated with stickers for gift giving.

Delta Soap Creations™, Fragrant Accents™, Finishing Touches™, Clear Glycerin, No Tip Mold

Footprint Rug
by Tracia Ledford Williams

Let's go tracking for forest animals like the white tailed deer, squirrel and maybe a wolf. Create a rug using carpet scraps and paint showing various animal prints.

You will need:

Vinyl flooring 36" x 24" (the pattern doesn't matter, we're using the back)
Acrylic paint - Ivory, Light Brown, Brown, Spice Brown, Yellow, Dark Green and Dark Orange
Exterior varnish
Die Cut Machine or scissors

Dies or patterns - paw prints
Scissors
Compressed sponges
Paint brushes
Sea sponge
Masking tape
Toothbrush
Pencil

1. Paint the backside of the vinyl piece with light ivory paint, let dry. Apply masking tape 2" from the edges, all the way around the floorcloth, creating a rectangle in the center.

2. Using a sea sponge, dip into light brown paint and apply around the border. Dip the same sponge into the brown paint and apply around the border allowing some of the first color to show through.

3. Using the die cut machine or pattern and scissors, cut out a large bear paw print from a piece of compressed sponge. Trace bird footprint on compressed sponge and cut out with scissors. Dip both sponges into water to expand, then wring out excess water.

4. Dip bear paw print into spice brown paint and apply to floor cloth. Dip bird foot print into yellow paint and apply to floor cloth.

5. Using round brush and dark green paint, paint zig zag lines around the border. Add orange dots around the footprints.

6. Dip toothbrush into brown paint, and spatter floorcloth. Let all paint dry. Using a large brush, apply 3 coats of varnish, allowing each coat to dry between applications.

Delta Ceramcoat® Acrylic Paint, Ceramcoat® Exterior/Interior Varnish; Eagle® Paintbrushes; Ellison® The Original Ellison® LetterMachine™, Decorative and Instructional Dies; Fiskars® Scissors; Darice® Compressed Sponges, Sea Sponge

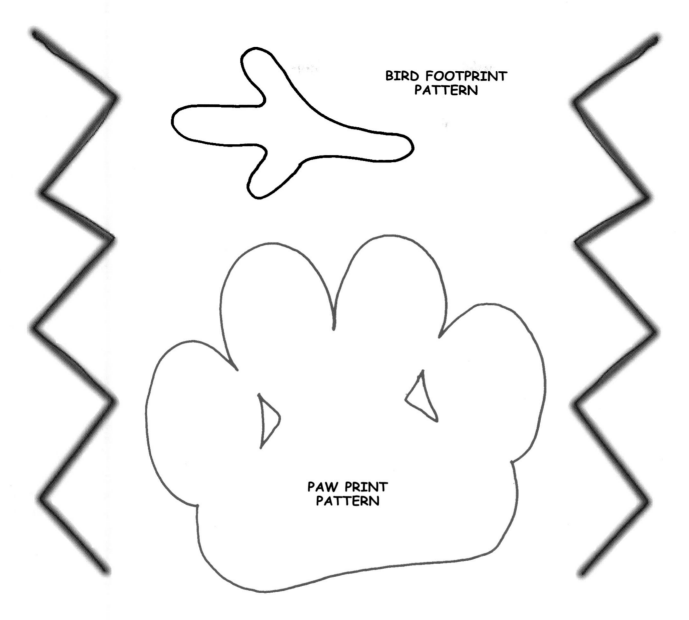

BIRD FOOTPRINT PATTERN

PAW PRINT PATTERN

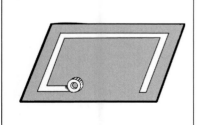

Use masking tape to make a border around edge.

Use toothbrush to spatter paint over floorcloth.

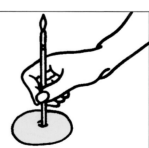

Dip paint brush handle in paint. Use to make dots.

DIE CUT DESIGNS © AND ™ OF ELLISON®

Hands On Crafts for Kids

Leaf Stamped Stationery

by Carol Scheffler

Oak, hickory, maple; which tree leaf will you choose for your stationary? Learn an easy technique to create your own stationary design from a leaf.

You will need:
Adhesive backed rubber
Leaf pattern or large punch
Acrylic stamp handle
6" square folded card - Pale Yellow
Markers - Pale Yellow and Red
Ink pads - Red ,Purple, Magenta and Teal
Ruler
"Thank You" rubber stamp
Pencil
Scissors

1. Trace and cut two leaf shapes from the adhesive backed rubber or use leaf hole punch.

2. Glue the die cut shapes directly on top of one another and then to the acrylic stamp handle.

3. Using the yellow marker, make a 2" circle on center of paper.

4. Tap the leaf stamp onto one of the inkpad colors.

5. Print several images randomly along the circle line, re-inking as necessary.

6. Change ink colors and continue stamping as described above. Don't be afraid to overlap leaves. The bottom leaf will show through.

7. Continue stamping until the circle line is completely covered with leaves creating a wreath.

8. Ink the rubber stamp with magenta then stamp "Thank You" in the center of the wreath, or write "Thank You" with a marker.

9. Using the ruler and red marker, draw a border around the outside edge of the card.

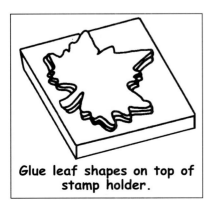

Glue leaf shapes on top of stamp holder.

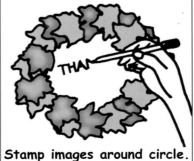

Stamp images around circle. Write message in center.

LEAF PATTERN

Ellison® Letter Machine, Instructional Dies, Self-Adhesive Rubber, Clear Plastic Stamp Mounts; Fiskars® Ruler, Scissors; Sakura of America Solid Markers

Forest Creature Pinata

by Danette Zurbuchen

Take a fun look at forest creatures with an owl pinata created from a paper bag. The bag shape is perfect for the owl, since they can't actually move their eyes and need to move their entire head to see. Their face is actually a flat disc with feathers at the edge to catch the slightest sound and aim the noise at their ears.

You will need:
Brown paper lunch bags
$\frac{1}{4}$" Hole punch
Candy
3' Length of yarn
Scissors
Tissue paper - Tan
Paper Crimper
Chenille stems - Black, Brown and Yellow
Thick white glue
Craft stick

1. Insert one lunch bag into another for added strength. Fold under the top edge $\frac{1}{4}$" twice.

2. Punch holes 1" apart around entire folded edge.

3. String yarn through holes to make a drawstring. Tip: Wrap tape around the end of the yarn to make the threading easier.

4. Fill the bag with candy to about 1" from the top.

5. Pull drawstring and tie in a knot.

6. Cut strips of tissue paper approximately 2" wide. Fold in half and crimp. Fringe by cutting from one edge to within $\frac{1}{2}$" of the other edge.

7. Apply glue with craft stick along uncut edge then glue the fringe around the bag near the bottom. Continue adding strips of fringe until the entire bag is covered.

8. Bend brown chenille stems for owl's "horns" and "wings". Glue to body. Tip: Punch holes in bag and insert ends of wings into holes. Secure with thick white glue.

9. Use yellow and black chenille stems to make eyes and yellow to make a beak. Glue the eyes onto the bag. Punch a hole in the bag with a pencil then glue the beak in place.

10. Break open your pinata with friends using a stick or bat and enjoy the candy inside!

Punch holes around top. Thread yarn through holes.

Cut folded tissue, or crepe paper into fringe.

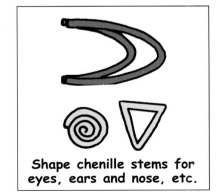

Shape chenille stems for eyes, ears and nose, etc.

Fiskars®Hand Punch, Paper Crimper, Scissors; Bemiss-Jason Rainbow® Bags, Spectra® Kolorfast® Tissue Paper, Yarn; Darice® Chenille Stems; Elmer's® Craft Bond™ Tacky Paste; Forster® Craft Sticks

Treasure Trees

by The Zurbuchen Family

Discover another use for paper bags as you create treasure trees for an enchanted forest. Glitter and beads and even some traditional leaves complete your project.

You will need:
Extra large brown paper lunch bag
Decorative gel glue
Glitter glue - assorted colors
Scraps of felt
Scissors
Ruler
Assorted beads and sequins

1. Open up a brown paper lunch bag. Press the bag down flat on one side, pushing the bottom side triangles out.

2. Starting at the top edge of the bag, use scissors to cut strips down the length of the bag measuring 8" long and 1" wide.

3. Hold the bag with two hands in the middle of the uncut portion of the bag. Twist the bag to make the trunk. Flatten the bottom of the bag so that the tree can stand on it's own.

4. Twist each of the 8" x 1" strips to make the tree branches.

5. Drizzle decorative gel glue over the entire tree and branches. Allow to dry.
Note: As the glue begins to dry, twist the tree trunk and each branch again.

6. Cut small, simple leaf shapes from the scraps of felt. Glue leaves in place along branches.

7. Use glitter glue to add accent color to branches and trunk. Glue beads and sequins randomly to trunk, base and branches. Allow to dry.

Cut paper bag into strips from top to bottom.

Twist strips together at the top of the bag.

Drizzle gel glue over branches. Allow to dry.

Elmer's® Galactic Glue™, 3D Glitter Paint Pens;
Darice® Beads, Sequins, Felt; Fiskars® Ruler, Scissors

Rubbings Journal

by Lynda Musante

Hardwood leaves are the basis for interesting rubbings and a journal to record your travels. Oil pastels and wire complement your journal.

You will need:
18 Gauge wire - Red
Oil pastels - Red, Orange and Yellow
Waffle paper - Brown and Yellow
Tracing paper
Lined paper
Decorative edge scissors
Hole punch
Glue
Pencil
Ruler
Paint brush
8" Twig
Oak leaf

1. Fold yellow and brown waffle paper in half. Tear brown paper in half and tear away all four edges. Glue to center front of yellow paper.

2. Place tracing paper over oak leaf. Use oil pastels and rub leaf impression onto paper in this order: red, orange and yellow. Use decorative edge scissors to cut out leaf. Glue paper and real leaves onto brown paper. Brush both leaves with glue to seal. Allow to dry.

3. Fold 4 or 5 lined pages in half. Insert into yellow cover. Measure and mark a spot 2" in from end and 1" in from fold. Repeat on other end. Punch holes at marked spots.

4. Cut a 12" length of red wire. Bend a spiral, using 2" on one end. Insert other end through punched holes from back to front of book. Hold twig in place and spiral wrap wire around twig up to other hole. Insert remaining wire through second hole. Cut to 2" and coil up end to secure.

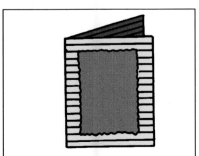

Fold corrugated paper in half. Glue torn paper to front.

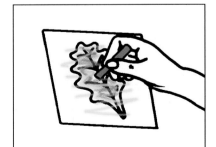

Place leaf under wax paper. Rub over with pastels.

Make holes in sides. Wrap wire around twig. Secure ends in holes.

Sakura of America Cray-Pas® Junior Artist Oil Pastels;
Bemiss-Jason Waffle Paper, Tracing Paper Pad; Fiskars® Paper Edgers, Hole punch, Ruler;
Darice® Wire; Elmer's® Craft Bond™ Paper Craft Glue Gel; Eagle® Paint Brush

Leis
by Carol Scheffler

A traditional sign of welcome made from the blooms of various island flowers, your tropical lei will never wilt when it's constructed from paper and beads.

You will need:
Die-Cut machine or scissors
Dies - 6 petal flower and birch leaf or patterns
Ridged paper - assorted colors
1/4" hole punch
Pony beads - assorted colors
String or cording - 2'
Paper Glue

DIE CUT DESIGNS © AND ™ OF ELLISON®

1. Using the die-cut machine and flower die, cut out about 15 flowers from various colors of ridged paper. Cut about 5 leaves from green ridged paper using the birch leaf die, or use pattern and scissors.

2. Punch a hole in each flower and leaf. About half of the items should be punched in their centers and half should be punched on their sides. This allows for more variation once they are strung together.

3. Thread flowers and leaves randomly onto cord. Place a bead between every other item. Rest the lei on the table so that the items lay flat and overlap each other. Wherever the items overlap, glue them together.

4. Continue stringing beads, flowers, and leaves in this fashion. Try to shape the items in a natural lei formation (in a deep "U" shape) before you glue them down.

5. Leave 10" at either end without anything strung on them.

6. Tie the lei around your neck.

FLOWER PATTERN

LEAF PATTERN

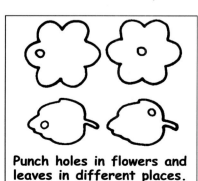

Punch holes in flowers and leaves in different places.

String together with beads between leaves and flowers.

Ellison® The Original Ellison® LetterMachine™, Decorative Dies; Fiskars® Hole Punch; Bemiss-Jason Corobuff® Sheets, Waffle Paper; Darice® Pony Beads, Cording; Elmer's® Craft Bond™ Paper Craft Glue Gel

THE TROPICS

Milk Jug Mask

by Debbi Kampel

Tropical paradises are often homes to unique cultures where ceremony is an important part of their tradition. Masks are an important part of this functional craft, but ours is even more useful since we use recycled milk jugs as the base of our mask.

You will need:
One gallon plastic milk jug
Egg carton
Cardboard tube
Acrylic paint - Blue, Red, Yellow and White
Acrylic varnish
Glitter paint pens - assorted colors
10-15 Pom poms - 7mm
2 Black beads - 12mm
Assorted feathers
Gel glue
Masking tape
Newspaper
Scissors
Ruler
Paint Brush
Container for glue/water mixture

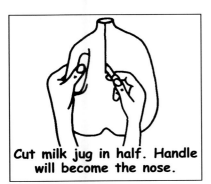

Cut milk jug in half. Handle will become the nose.

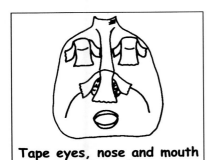

Tape eyes, nose and mouth pieces in place.

1. Have an adult help you cut the milk jug in half from top to bottom, making sure that the handle is in the middle on one side. The handle will form the bridge of the nose.

2. Cut two cells from the egg carton. Use masking tape to secure these cells in place on either side of the nose, for the eyes.

3. Form a ball of newspaper for the base of the nose and tape in place.

4. Cut a 1" section of cardboard tube and tape in place for mouth.

5. Mix one part gel glue with one part water in container. Tear newspaper into lengthwise strips, approximately 1" wide. Dip one strip at a time into glue/water mixture. Pull paper strip upward, between two fingers, to remove excess glue. Apply these strips to the milk carton and added facial features to completely cover them. Apply two layers of newspaper strips. Allow to dry. Note: This can take 1-3 days, depending on humidity.

6. Use acrylic paint to paint the nose yellow, the mouth red, the eyes white and the face blue. Allow to dry. Brush with a light coat of acrylic varnish.

7. Glue pompoms in place above eyes for eyebrows. Glue a black bead to the center of each eye. Glue feathers to the back of the milk carton spout for hair.

8. Decorate mask with glitter pens as desired.

Elmer's® 3D Glitter Paint Pens, School Glue Gel;
Delta Ceramcoat® Acrylic Paint, Ceramcoat® Exterior/Interior Varnish;
Fiskars® Scissors, Ruler; Eagle® Paint Brush; Darice® Pompoms, Feathers, Beads

Frogs and Footprints

by Tracia Ledford Williams

About ⅘th's of all of the frog and toad species live in subtropical rain forests. They like the warmth and dampness. Many of these frogs have some special characteristics. For example, Costa Rican Flying frogs are named because of the way they "fly" from tree to tree. Green Tree frogs look like a bud on a branch, and there are many more. Choose a special trait for your frog as you paint him across a shirt.

You will need:
White T-shirt
Fabric dye - Green, Yellow, Orange, Black and Bright Pink
Paintbrushes
Cardboard
Masking Tape
Toothbrush
Compressed Sponge
Scissors
Black permanent pen
Pencil
Paper plate

1. Place pre-washed T-shirt over cardboard. Secure with masking tape.

2. Place the pattern under the shirt then trace design with the black permanent pen.

3. Paint frogs green, then add yellow fabric paint to his back and orange to his tummy area. Add a black dot, using the handle of the paint brush to paint his eyes.

4. Trace leaf pattern on compressed sponge, cut with scissors and expand in water. Wring out excess water. Pour a puddle of yellow fabric paint and a puddle of green fabric paint next to each other on a paper plate, dip sponge part way into each color, then apply to shirt. Apply as many leaves as you like, around the frogs.

5. Mix a few drops of orange and green fabric paint together then, using a round brush, paint vines connecting leaves around and from underneath the frogs.

6. Dip paint brush handle into orange fabric paint. Apply dots around the vines.

7. Dip moist toothbrush into bright pink fabric paint, drag thumb across bristles to spatter the paint over the T-shirt.

Trace pattern then transfer onto sponge.

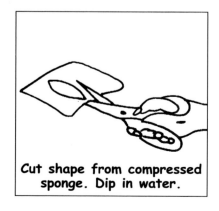

Cut shape from compressed sponge. Dip in water.

Use toothbrush to spatter paint on shirt.

THE TROPICS

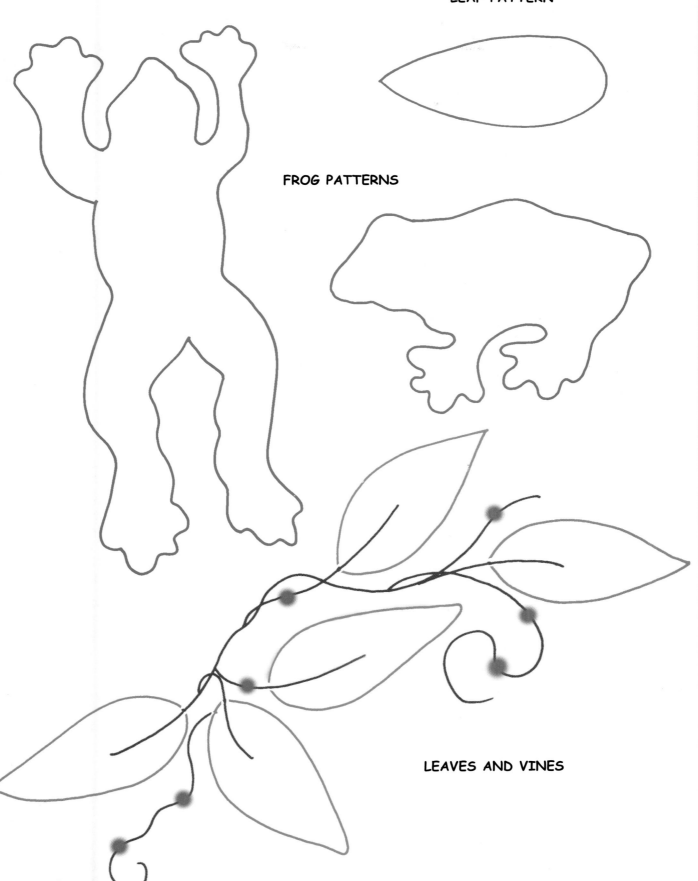

LEAF PATTERN

FROG PATTERNS

THE TROPICS

LEAVES AND VINES

Peacock

by Julie McGuffee

One of the most beautiful birds in the world, peacocks are actually a native of India and Ceylon, but have been introduced to most corners of the world. The island temperature seems to suit them! The male peacock has the beautiful blue feathers. Use oil pastels to create them for your project.

You will need:
4" Styrofoam cone
2" Styrofoam egg
2½" Styrofoam ball
Non-bleeding tissue paper - Green
Acrylic paint - Blue, Black & White
Paintbrush
White glue
White cardstock
Oil Pastel crayons
Scissors
2 Yellow chenille stems
Bumpy Royal Blue chenille
2 Wiggle eyes
Orange construction paper
Blue glitter glue
Craft sticks

1. Using a plastic knife, cut the styrofoam ball in half. Glue one half to the base of the cone.

2. Tear the green tissue paper into 1" pieces. Glue to the surface of the cone and the styrofoam egg. Let dry, then paint over surface with a light coat of blue paint. Re-paint the styrofoam with blue glitter glue.
Note: Push a craft stick into the top of the cone to use for a handle while painting.

3. Using pattern, trace 7 tail feathers onto the white cardstock. Color circles at the top of the feathers then completely cover the tails with dark green, then dark blue crayons. Cut out. Use the paintbrush handle to scratch vein lines on the feathers. Draw one straight line down the center of the feather, then lines from the center to the outside edge of the feather. Arrange feathers in a fan shape then glue together.

4. Paint each side of the head with black. Glue wiggle eyes in place then paint a white stroke underneath each eye.

5. Cut a 1½" x 1½" square of orange construction paper. Fold in half diagonally then cut along the fold line. Roll one triangle into a cone for the beak. Overlap ends, then glue in place. Glue the beak to the pointed end of the head then glue the head to the top of the cone.

6. Cut three royal blue chenille bumps. Pierce three holes along the top of the head with a toothpick then glue the three bumps in place.

7. Glue the tail to the back of the body. Hold in place with quilt pins.

8. To make legs, fold one end of yellow chenille stem to make feet. Fold opposite end down to feet. Twist together. Insert folded end into the base of the body. Make two.

9. Glue each foot to a craftstick so your peacock will stand.

Dow Styrofoam® Brand Plastic Foam; Bemiss Jason Spectra® Tissue Paper, Construction Paper; Delta Ceramcoat® Acrylic Paint; Eagle® Paint Brush; Elmer's® School Glue, 3D Glitter Paint Pens; Sakura of America Cray-Pas® Oil Pastels; Fiskars® Scissors; Darice® Chenille Stems, Wiggle Eyes

THE TROPICS

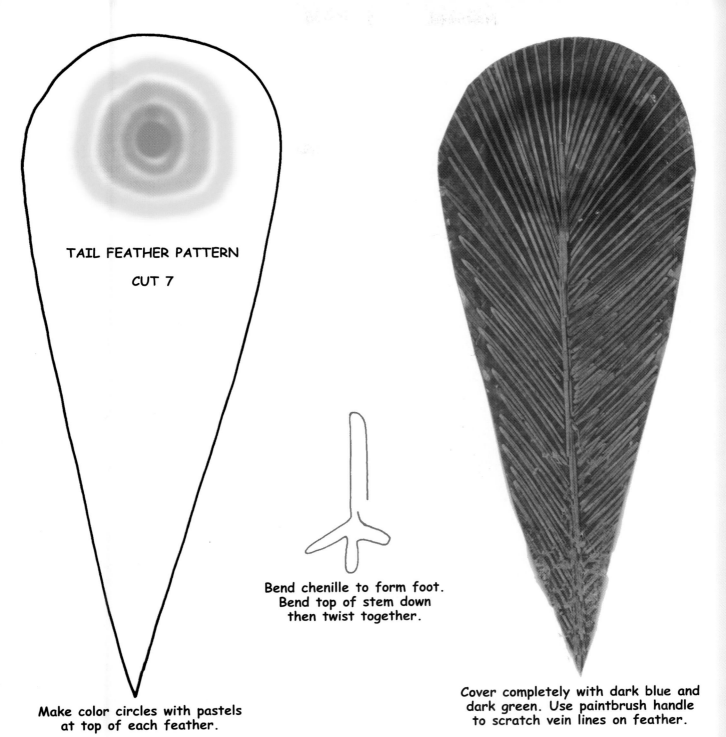

TAIL FEATHER PATTERN

CUT 7

Make color circles with pastels
at top of each feather.

Bend chenille to form foot.
Bend top of stem down
then twist together.

Cover completely with dark blue and
dark green. Use paintbrush handle
to scratch vein lines on feather.

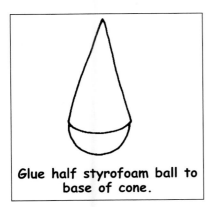

Glue half styrofoam ball to
base of cone.

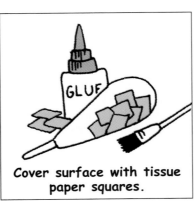

Cover surface with tissue
paper squares.

Paint side of head black.
Add white under eye.

Fuzzy Parrot

by Patty Cox

There are over 300 species of parrots. Make a scarlet macaw of chenille and Styrofoam. This beautiful parrot is declining in numbers due to the destruction of the rainforest. It is native to Mexico, South America and Central America.

You will need:
2½" Styrofoam ball
3³⁄₁₆" x 2³⁄₁₆" Styrofoam egg
12" x 6mm chenille stems - 50 Red,
 18 Blue, 8 Yellow and 6 green
Foam sheets - Yellow and Black
Adhesive foam sheet - White
2 Wiggle eyes - 12mm
2 Yellow 1" spring clothespins
Scissors
Glue
Straight pins
Toothpicks
Pencil
Jumbo craft stick
Optional: wire hanger and paper ribbon

1. Press and flatten one side of styrofoam ball and the large end of the egg on tabletop. Insert two toothpicks into flattened side of egg. Push toothpicks into flattened side of ball securing the two shapes together.

2. Draw color placement with pencil, draw two ovals on each side of body for wing placement. Draw a circle in the top of each oval for wing top. Draw a "V" on front of body for belly.

3. Fold blue chenille stems for wings as shown. Insert wings into parrot sides. Fold red and blue chenille stems for tail as shown. Insert tail into parrot body base.

4. Wrap a chenille stem around a jumbo craft stick six times. Begin and end with about 1" ends. Bend ends at a 90º angle. Stick ends into styrofoam body base. Begin at bottom of bird and work up, slightly overlapping each row following color guide.

5. Cut beak shapes from craft foam. Fold lower beak in half. Use two straight pins to secure beak to front of face. Fold beak top in half. Pin beak on top of lower beak. Cut face side pieces from white adhesive foam. Stick face sides on each side of beak. Glue wiggle eyes on each side of face.

6. Cut a 4" length of red chenille stem. Thread stem through spring opening of clothespins. Insert stem ends with clothespin "feet" into parrot's lower body.

7. **Optional:** Bend a wire hanger into a circle. Clip parrot's feet onto ring. Add additional wire to support parrot in ring as needed. Add a paper ribbon bow at hanger top.

Dow Styrofoam® Brand Plastic Foam;
Darice® Foamies™, Pre-Adhesive Foamies™, Wiggle Eyes, Chenille Stems, Paper Ribbon; Forster® Spring Clothespins, Jumbo Craft Sticks, Toothpicks; Elmer's® White School Glue; Fiskars® Scissors

THE TROPICS

UPPER BEAK PATTERN

CUT 1 YELLOW

LOWER BEAK PATTERN

CUT 1 BLACK

FACE SIDE PATTERN

**CUT 2 WHITE
(ONE REVERSE)**

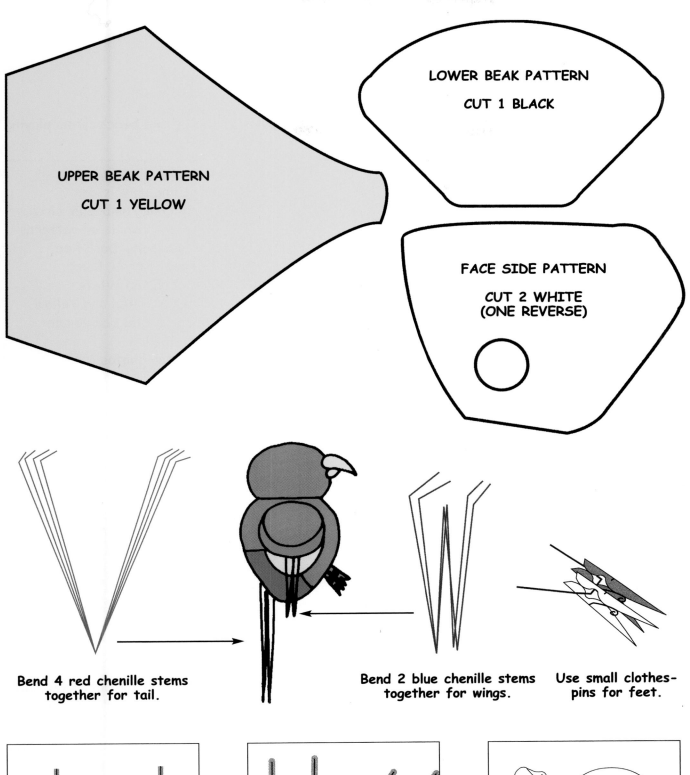

Bend 4 red chenille stems together for tail.

Bend 2 blue chenille stems together for wings.

Use small clothespins for feet.

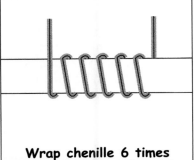

Wrap chenille 6 times around jumbo craft stick.

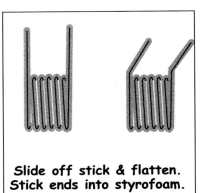

Slide off stick & flatten. Stick ends into styrofoam.

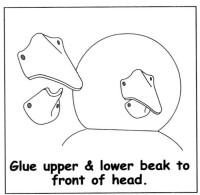

Glue upper & lower beak to front of head.

Hands On Crafts for Kids

Sand Sculpture

by Sandi Genovese

This unique 3D sand sculpture conjures up all of the popular images of the beach; from playing in the water, to beach umbrellas and ocean creatures.

You will need:
Die-cut machine or scissors
Dies - beach chair, umbrella, circles, waves and killer whale or patterns
Construction paper - Dark Red, Black, Yellow, Green, Blue, Turquoise, Tan and White
Patterned paper - Red and Yellow
13"x 9" x 2¼" Metal baking pan
Metal paint - Yellow
Beach and water photos (copies)
Sticker borders
Glue stick
Sand
Sea shells
Skewers

1. To create the beach themed sand sculpture, paint a metal baking pan with yellow metal paint. Decorate the sides with sticker borders then fill the pan with sand.

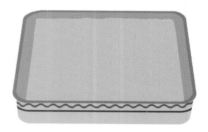

2. Die-cut the beach umbrella out of four different colors or use pattern and scissors. Using the perforation line as a guide, trim the brown handle and glue it to the dark red base. Trim the white and the patterned umbrellas along the perforation lines and glue the pieces to the dark red base as shown. Make a second umbrella, this time embellishing the reverse side. Spread glue on the backs of both umbrellas then glue together around a skewer. Leave the pointed end of the skewer exposed.

Ellison® The Original Ellison® LetterMachine™, Decorative and Instructional Dies; Bemiss Jason Spectra® Construction Paper, Patterned Paper; Fiskars® Scissors; Elmer's® Craft Bond™ Glue Stick; Forster® Skewers; Delta Air-Dry PermEnamel™ Paint

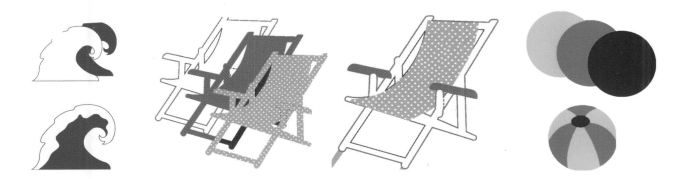

3. Repeat this process with each of the other die-cuts in the beach scene then place the embellished die-cuts in the sand.

4. To create pairs of photos, color copy the photo in its original form and as a mirror image. (Most color copy machines have this feature). Trim around the subject of the photo. Glue the backs of the photographs together around a wooden skewer. Repeat the process with other photos then place in the sand to complete the sand sculpture. Sea shells can also be included if desired.

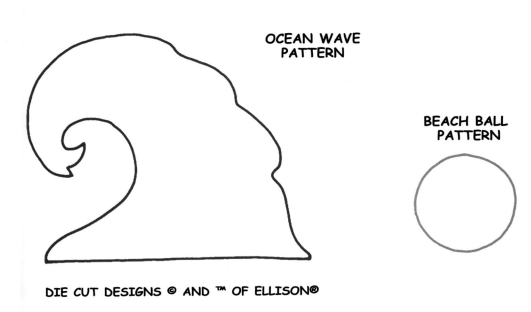

OCEAN WAVE
PATTERN

BEACH BALL
PATTERN

DIE CUT DESIGNS © AND ™ OF ELLISON®

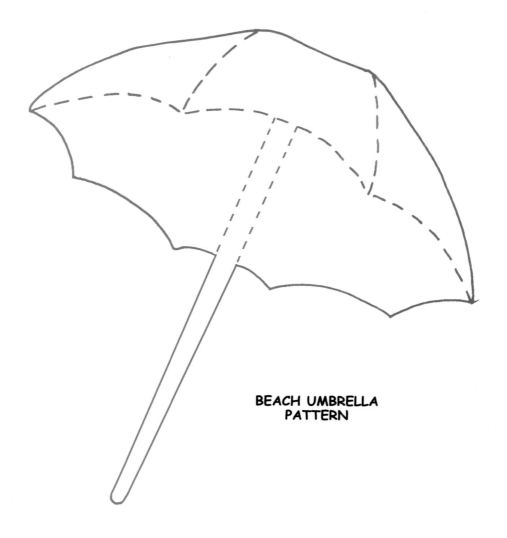

BEACH UMBRELLA PATTERN

BEACH CHAIR PATTERN

DIE CUT DESIGNS © AND ™ OF ELLISON®

Hands On Crafts for Kids

Sand Cast Sea Treasures

by Brenda Spitzer

Learn to cast your own seashell treasures and add a little glitter to bring out their true beauty.

You will need:
Starfish or shells found on the beach
4 Cups sand
Clear plastic pony beads - Yellow
  and Purple
Decorative gel glue
White glue
Plaster of Paris
Glitter glue - Green and Purple
2 Containers for sand and plaster mixture
Spoon
Paint brush
Water

AT THE BEACH

1. Collect shells or starfish on the beach. If you do not live near a beach, these items are often available at craft stores.

2. Fill container with four cups of sand. Add ½ cup of water to sand and mix well.

3. Press starfish or shell, face down into sand to make an impression. Remove shell from sand.

4. In another container, mix ½ bottle of white glue with ½ cup of water. Add 1 cup of plaster of Paris. Mix well. Tip: This step is messy. Work outside if possible.

5. Pour this plaster mixture into impression in the sand. Allow this to set for one hour. Remove plaster casting from sand. Brush off extra sand with a paint brush.

6. Brush a coat of decorative gel glue over the top surface of sand casting. Outline and add accents with glitter glue. Glue pony beads to sand castings.

Press shell into sand and water mixture.

Mix water, white glue and plaster of Paris.

Pour mixture into depression in sand.

Elmer's® Galactic Glue™, 3D Glitter Paint Pens, White School Glue; Darice® Pony Beads, Sand; Eagle® Golden Taklon Brush

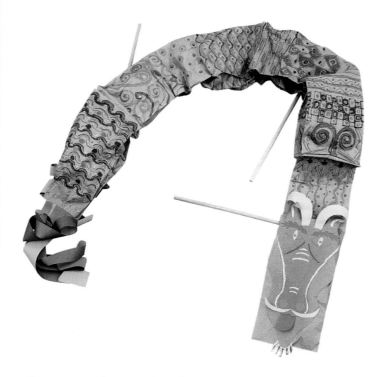

Paper Bag Dragon
by The May Family

Lets go fly a kite; a paper bag dragon perfect for catching the wind at the beach. When you're not at the beach it would also be the ideal highlight at a Chinese New Year celebration.

You will need:
7 Extra large brown lunch bags
7 Sheets tissue paper
Oil pastels - assorted colors
Glitter paint pens - assorted colors
Construction Paper 9" x 12" sheets - Red, Green and Yellow and 2 Purple,
Two 12" x 18" two tone paper sheets -
  Red/Green and Green/Green
3 Wooden dowels - 12" x $\frac{3}{8}$"
Scissors
Ruler
White glue
Stapler
Masking tape

1. Using oil pastels, draw colorful patterns on top and sides of six bags. Your patterns might include scales, stripes, dots, zigzag lines and diamonds.

2. Use glitter paint pens to outline patterns or add accents. Allow to dry.

3. Use patterns to trace dragon face and features onto construction paper. Cut out. Glue face to top side of remaining bag. Glue features in place as indicated in picture. Add more details to face with oil pastels and glitter paint pens, if desired. Allow to dry.

4. Lightly crumple a sheet of tissue paper and stuff inside of each bag.

5. Assemble the dragon by stapling the open edges of the first two bags and then stapling the bottom edges of bags two and three. Staple open edges of bags three and four. Continue, alternating along the entire length of the dragon. Note: Before stapling edges of bags, spread white glue between the bottoms of the bags.

6. Cut the two tone paper into 18" x 1½" strips. Roll strips around a pen or a paint brush to curl. Staple ends of paper strips inside the open end of the last bag.

7. To parade with the dragon, tape one end of each dowel rod to bottom of dragon. One will be placed near the front, in the middle and in the back. Your dragon is now ready for the parade!

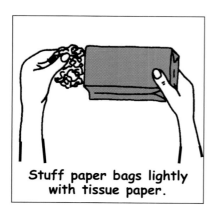
Stuff paper bags lightly with tissue paper.

Fold top closed. Spread glue on bottom of bags.

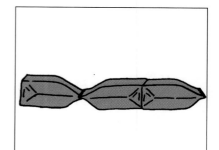
Glue bottoms of bags; staple tops of bags together.

Sakura of America Cray-Pas® Junior Artist Oil Pastels; Elmer's® 3D Glitter Paint Pens, White School Glue; Fiskars® Ruler, Scissors; Bemiss-Jason Fadeless® Duet Sheets, Rainbow® Construction Paper, Spectra® Tissue Paper; Forster® Wooden Dowels

Hands On Crafts for Kids

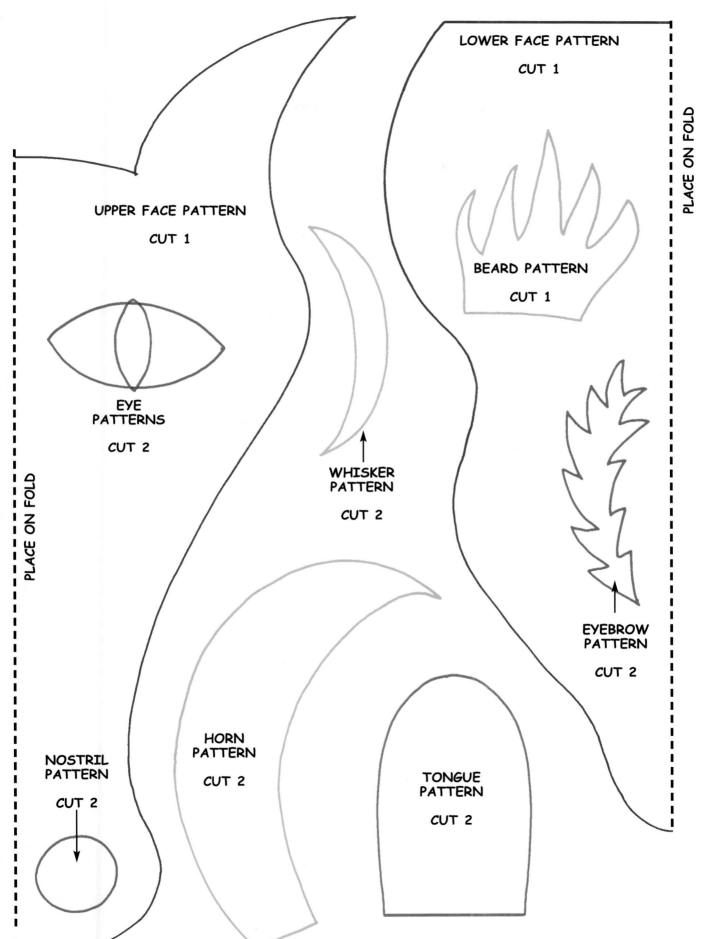

LOWER FACE PATTERN

CUT 1

PLACE ON FOLD

UPPER FACE PATTERN

CUT 1

BEARD PATTERN

CUT 1

EYE PATTERNS

CUT 2

PLACE ON FOLD

WHISKER PATTERN

CUT 2

EYEBROW PATTERN

CUT 2

AT THE BEACH

NOSTRIL PATTERN

CUT 2

HORN PATTERN

CUT 2

TONGUE PATTERN

CUT 2

Sand Castle

by Kathleen George

This is one sand castle that won't be washed away by the tide! Real sand, glue, styrofoam and paper rolls are all you need.

You will need:
Styrofoam sheet - 4" x 6" x 1"
2 or more Styrofoam cones 4 ½"
3-5 Cardboard tubes
Acrylic paint - Tan
White sand
Foam sheet - any color
Toothpicks
Stiff paint brush
White school glue
Box lid
Scissors
Masking tape
Thin cardboard

1. Round the corners of 4" x 6" Styrofoam base by pressing on a hard surface.

2. Cut cardboard tubes into different lengths (4" - 8").

3. Glue a Styrofoam cone onto two or three of the tubes.

4. Using pattern, cut a strip of thin cardboard to be used for the battlement. Wrap around the top of the remaining tubes. Glue in place. Hold together with a small piece of masking tape until glue dries.

5. Assemble the tube towers on top of the base the way you want. Twist the tubes down into the surface of the styrofoam firmly about ¼" then remove. Do not glue in place at this point.

6. Paint all the castle parts with tan paint. Let dry thoroughly.

7. Spread thin craft glue evenly over a section of the castle using a stiff paint brush. Sprinkle sand onto the glue. Gently press the sand into the glue with your fingertips. Shake excess sand off over a box lid and continue the gluing procedure until the whole castle, tubes and base are covered with sand. You can choose if you want to cover the inside of the tubes with sand or not. Note: Be sure not to fill in the tube tower depressions in the base. You will need to push the towers back into these depressions when you assemble the castle.

8. Fill the depressions with glue then twist the towers back into their places on the base.

9. Cut out flags from colorful foam. Glue the flags onto toothpicks and stick the toothpicks into the top of the cones with a drop of glue.

10. Decorate the castle with shells, if desired.

Dow Styrofoam® Brand Plastic Foam; Delta Ceramcoat® Acrylic Paint; Darice® Foamies™, Sand; Eagle® Paint Brush; Elmer's® School Glue; Forster® Toothpicks; Fiskars® Scissors

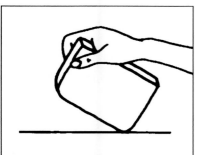

Round styrofoam corners on counter top.

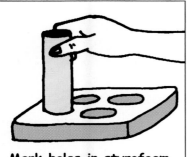

Mark holes in styrofoam for castle towers.

Glue styrofoam cone to top of some towers.

Tape battlements around tops of other towers.

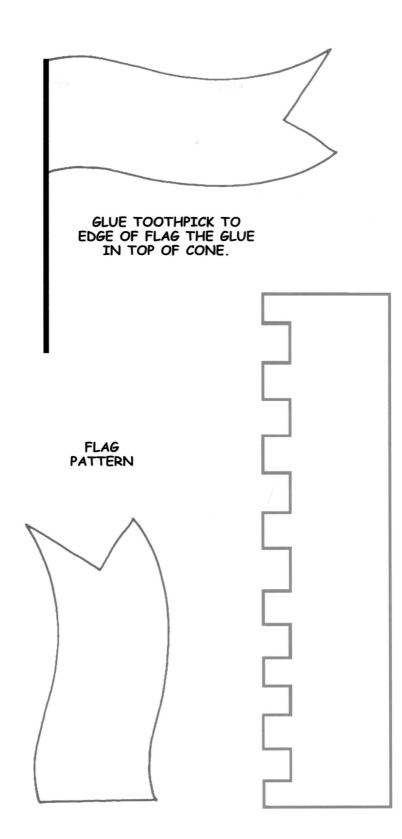

GLUE TOOTHPICK TO
EDGE OF FLAG THE GLUE
IN TOP OF CONE.

FLAG
PATTERN

BATTLEMENTS
PATTERN

Hands On Crafts for Kids

Sea Creatures
by Dimensions®

Your sand castle won't be complete without a few inhabitants. Try this easy bead craft to make an ocean full of sea creatures.

You will need:
Perler beads - assorted colors
Adhesive backed patterns

1. Choose adhesive backed patterns.

2. Remove backing paper one section at a time, then add beads in your choice of colors.

3. Continue adding beads to each section of design until the pattern is completely covered.

Dimensions® Perler Beads and Adhesive Patterns

Fish Abstract

by Ana and Suzi Richters

This exotic mobile uses varied techniques to create a fish collage from netting, beads and lace. You can even incorporate bits of shells and driftwood from a long walk on the beach.

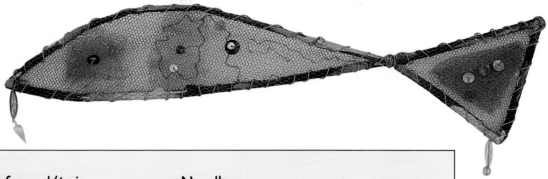

You will need:

Flexible piece of wood/twig	Needle
Acrylic paint - Red, Yellow, Blue, Green, Purple and White	Monofilament
	Scissors
Netting or tulle - two or three colors	Paint Brush
	Craft stick
Sequins and beads	Thick white glue
Crochet cotton or embroidery floss	String

1. Turn the wood or twig in all directions to discover what your imagination "sees" in it. Feel free to bend or join it with other pieces of wood or natural materials.

2. Stabilize the form you want with string and strong glue. Let dry.

3. Basecoat the wood with paint then let dry. Paint decorative patterns with additional colors.

4. Lay one or more layers of netting or tulle on a table top. Experiment with two or more colors layered together. Place your wood shape on top of the netting then cut netting to fit the shape. It should extend to the outside edges of the wood form.

5. Using a craft stick, apply glue to several points on the wood form then press the netting into the glue. Let dry.

6. Use needle and crochet cotton to whip stitch netting to form. You now have your basic transparent form.

7. Cut smaller pieces of netting or other translucent materials and lay these on the form, creating pleasing patterns. Secure these with more stitching, which can become another decorative element. Have fun with the stitches. They don't need to be perfect or strong, just enough to hold the additional embellishment to the basic form. Add beads, sequins, buttons or other decorations as you like. Remember, this will be viewed from both sides, so keep that in mind as you decorate.

8. Hold the finished piece by its top edge to find the balance point then tie monofilament around it, knotting securely. Hang from the ceiling so it can rotate freely in the breeze.

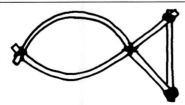

Tie twigs together into a shape resembling a fish.

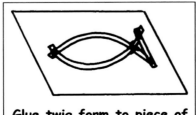

Glue twig form to piece of tulle or lacey fabric.

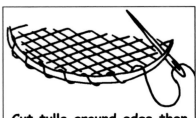

Cut tulle around edge then stitch in place.

Delta® Acrylic Paint; Darice® Sequins, Beads, Monofilament; Eagle® Paint Brushes; Elmer's® White School Glue and Tacky Paste; Fiskars® Scissors

Just Floating Along
by Kathleen George

There are actually 2 types of icebergs, tabular or flat tops and glacier, which have a higher area above water. In both cases most of the iceberg is actually below the water. Only 1/8 is above the surface! Watch some penguins having fun on the surface of an Antarctic tabular iceberg.

You will need:
8 Styrofoam sheets - 6" x 9" x 1"
Plastic wrap - Blue
Tissue paper - Blue
Craft paste
Gel glue
Plastic knife
Paint brush
Wave edge scissors

Iceberg

1. Stack sheets of styrofoam together until they are 8" high. Glue together with a generous amount of craft paste. Allow to dry.

2. Cut away sides of styrofoam block to represent melting and ice cracks on an iceberg. Save scraps.

3. Working on one side at a time, spread gel glue all over the surface of the styrofoam from the bottom of the iceberg to 1" from the top. Lay the plastic wrap carefully over the glue and gently pat down the plastic wrap so that there are no air pockets. A few wrinkles will resemble random cracks in the iceberg. Glue the plastic wrap over the remaining 3 sides. Stretch the excess plastic wrap around to the bottom, trim bulky amount away and glue the wrap down against the bottom.

4. Cut a strip of blue tissue paper about ½" wide with decorative scissors to represent the waves on the water. Glue the strip exactly 1" down from the top of the iceberg.

5. Glue styrofoam scraps to top.

Chip away corner edges of styrofoam block.

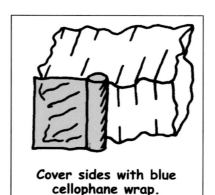

Cover sides with blue cellophane wrap.

Glue additional pieces to top of iceberg.

Dow Styrofoam® Brand Plastic Foam; Delta Ceramcoat® Acrylic Paint; Darice® Beads, Felt; Eagle® Paint Brush; Elmer's® School Glue Gel, Craft Bond™ Tacky Paste, Forster® Skewers; Bemiss-Jason Spectra® Tissue Paper; Fiskars Scissors & Paper Edgers

You will need:
2 3/8" x 1 7/8" Styrofoam egg
1" Styrofoam ball
Acrylic paint - Black and Orange
2 Beads - Black
Felt - Black, Orange or Gray
Toothpick
Paint brush
Craft glue

Penguin

1. Slice a bit from the top and bottom of the styrofoam egg. Press the styrofoam ball onto the top of the egg until it fits tightly. Glue in place and let dry.

2. Paint the black area. Tip: Push a craft stick into the bottom of the penguin to make it easier to hold while painting. Place the craft stick and penguin into a glass to dry.

3. Cut out wings, tail and feet from felt and glue in place with white craft glue.

4. Cut 1/2" piece from toothpick and paint orange. Push blunt edge into head for beak.

5. Glue two beads to head for eyes.

6. Make more penguins to keep your first penguin company!

TAIL
PATTERN
BLACK

WING
PATTERN
BLACK

FEET
PATTERN
GRAY or ORANGE

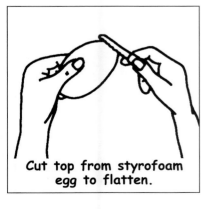

Cut top from styrofoam egg to flatten.

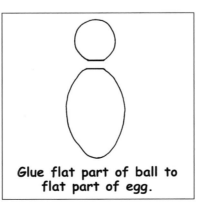

Glue flat part of ball to flat part of egg.

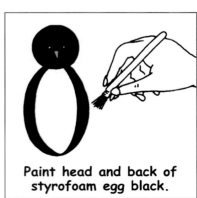

Paint head and back of styrofoam egg black.

Inukshuk

by Kathleen George

An Inukshuk is a small pile of stones arranged in the likeness of a person. The Inuit people used them as trail markers, indicating safe passage. Our stones are actually made of styrofoam and very light weight.

You will need:
Scraps of 1" and 2" Styrofoam sheets
Tissue paper - Black and White
Glue
Tacky paste
1" Paint brush
Wooden skewers
Toothpicks
Serrated knife

1. Cut scraps of styrofoam sheets into irregular shapes to look like rocks. Vary the size and shape. Be sure and create a few that are extra long. Continue shaping the rocks by pushing and rolling the cut edges against a tabletop.

2. Tear tissue paper into 2" x 2" rectangles. Make some large and smaller pieces.

3. Push a wooden skewer into each rock to hold while working on it. Spread glue generously all over the rock with a wide paint brush. Lay a piece of black tissue paper onto the rock and brush more glue on top of it. Proceed to cover the rest of the rocks with black tissue in the same manner.

4. Glue a layer of white tissue over top of the black tissue in the same manner. Brush the second layer on firmly, flattening any folds and smoothing wrinkles out as much as possible.

5. Place the skewer into a glass and allow the rock to dry thoroughly. This may take overnight.

6. When all the rocks are dry twist the skewers to remove. Stack the rocks so they roughly resemble a man with his arms out. Use the big rocks as feet and legs and the long rocks as arms. Use toothpicks to hold rocks together then glue in place.

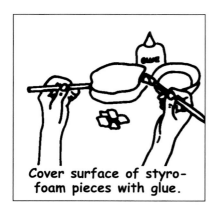

Cover surface of styrofoam pieces with glue.

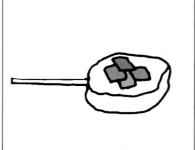

Cover pieces with tissue, then brush more glue on top.

Glue pieces together. Hold in place with toothpicks.

Dow Styrofoam® Brand Plastic Foam; Eagle® Paint Brush; Elmer's® School Glue, Craft Bond™ Tacky Paste; Forster® Skewers and Toothpicks; Bemiss-Jason Spectra® Tissue Paper

Polar Bears

by Tracia Ledford Williams

What's white and fuzzy, but not really cuddly? A polar bear! Just remember these are real bears that grow to over 10 feet long, and males weigh up to 1300 pounds. Our polar bear design is made from paint and is definitely a more cuddly type.

You will need:

Composition book	Stencil sponges
Gesso	Black permanent pen
Paper paint - assorted	Sparkle glaze
colors	Paint brushes
Alphabet stencil	Paper towels
	Pencil

1. Using a large brush, cover the surface of the book with gesso. Let dry.

2. Dip a piece of paper towel into water to moisten and then into blue paper paint, tap over surface of book to speckle the background.

3. Trace and transfer the polar bear pattern to the front of the book. Mix a tiny amount of yellow with gesso and paint the polar bear, let it dry. Outline and add eyes and a nose with black permanent pen.

4. Cut stencil sponge into 4 pieces. Dip one piece into blue and apply under polar bear.

5. Using sponge pieces, and various colors of paper paint, use the alphabet stencil to apply words (your name, the word polar bear) above the polar bear.

6. Dip a square stencil sponge into the yellow and add the checkerboard edge to the binding of the book. Add various dots of paper paint on the yellow squares. Let all paint dry.

7. Apply sparkle glaze over the entire cover to add a glistening finish.

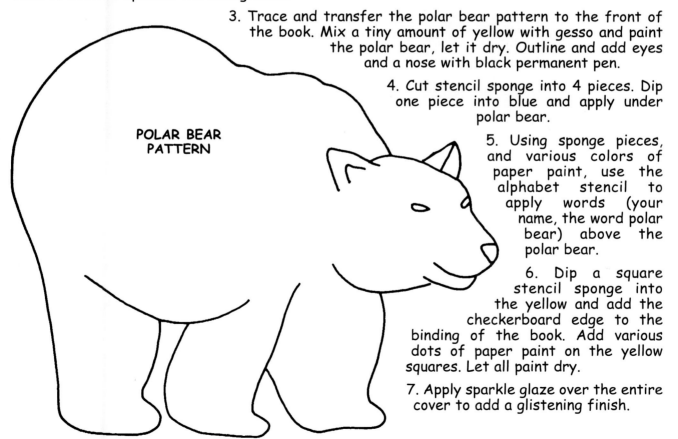

POLAR BEAR PATTERN

Delta Ceramcoat® Sparkle Glaze™, Cherished Memories™ Acid-Free Paper Paint, Ceramcoat® Gesso, Stencil Magic® Pre-Cut Decorative Stencils, Cherished Memories™ Stencil Buddy™, Stencil Sponges; Eagle® Brush Kid's Brushes; Sakura of America IDenti-pen™

Sparkling Snowflakes

by Brenda Spitzer

We all know that no two snowflakes are alike! Create your own design with sparkling highlights made from glue.

You will need:

Glitter glue - Blue	Decorative thread	Ruler
9" x 12" Sheet clear	Paper	Masking tape
plastic mylar	Scissors	Protractor
	Needle	Pencil

1. Use ruler and pencil to draw a snowflake pattern on paper, or use the patterns provided. To make a 6 point snowflake draw center dot then make marks at 0º, 60º, 120º, 180º. Turn and do the same for the other half. Fill in with some additional shapes and lines.

2. Place sheet of clear plastic mylar over the snowflake drawing. Hold in place with masking tape.

3. Trace over lines of pattern with blue glitter glue, or other color if desired. Allow to dry.

4. Cut around the snowflake close to the edge of the glitter glue.

5. Use a needle to run a piece of thread through one point of the snowflake for a hanger. Knot the ends of the thread.

6. You can leave the mylar behind the snowflake or peel the snowflake from the mylar once it has dried completely.

Elmer's® 3D Glitter Paint Pens; Fiskars® Ruler, Scissors, Protractor

SNOWFLAKE PATTERNS

Hands On Crafts for Kids

Arctic Bookmark Magnets

by Sandi Genovese

Some of the inhabitants of the Arctic have come in from the cold as a paper bookmark. You'll never lose your place with this unique method involving magnets.

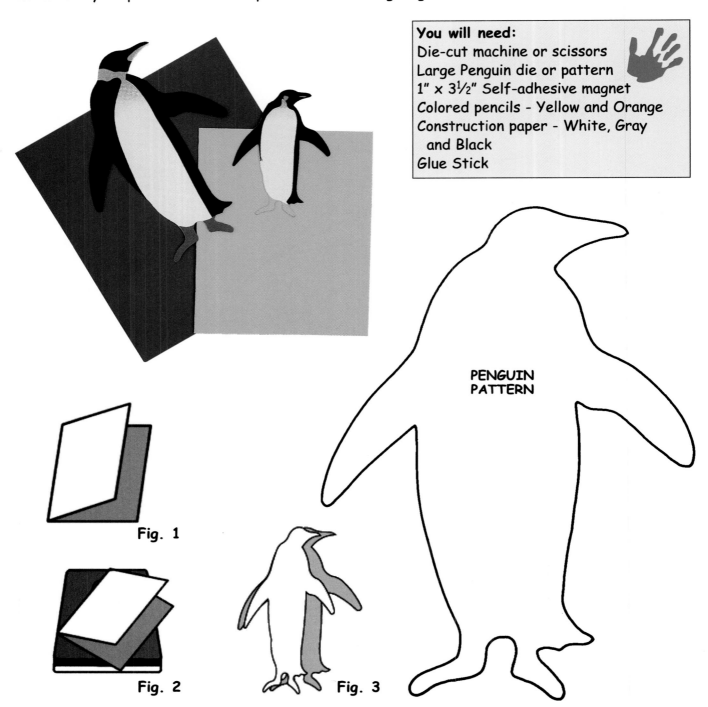

You will need:
Die-cut machine or scissors
Large Penguin die or pattern
1" x 3½" Self-adhesive magnet
Colored pencils - Yellow and Orange
Construction paper - White, Gray and Black
Glue Stick

PENGUIN PATTERN

Fig. 1

Fig. 2   Fig. 3

1. Fold white paper in half first before cutting large penguin (Fig. 1). Position the die so the folded paper remains intact at the penguin's upper back (blade must be exposed) (Fig. 2). Cut to create a penguin booklet (Fig. 3) or use pattern and scissors.

2. Cut an additional black and gray penguin.

3. Trim the gray feet and glue to the front of the white penguin booklet.

4. Cut the black penguin elements and glue to the front of the white penguin booklet.

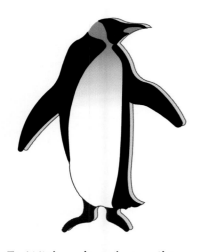

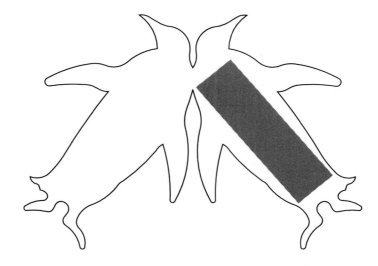

5. With colored pencils create the orange and yellow shading on the penguin's head and chest.

6. Cut the self-adhesive magnet into two 1" x 3½" strips . Place the strips, together, magnet sides touching. Keeping the two strips together, peel the backing off one side of the magnet and fasten to the inside of the penguin booklet.

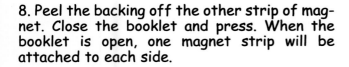

8. Peel the backing off the other strip of magnet. Close the booklet and press. When the booklet is open, one magnet strip will be attached to each side.

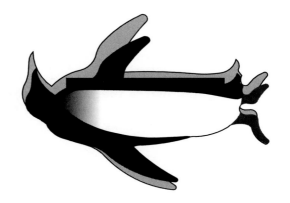

Bleach Bottle Fish

by Tarah Cunningham,
Laura and Sue Bruns

You might not see this exact fish along the coral reef, but you will see the same bright colors in many of the fish.

You will need:
Empty, clean laundry detergent jug
Construction paper
Tissue paper - assorted colors
Crepe paper streamers - assorted colors
Scissors
Double sided tape
Glue
Craft stick
Paste
Paint pens
Yarn

1. Cut pieces of construction paper large enough to glue over the labels on the jug.

2. Turn jug on its side, with the handle on top. Make two eyes from construction paper and glue to front of fish.

3. Cut four strips of tissue paper in graduated widths, nested and folded together, with the narrowest strip on the outside.

4. Open the outer strip and glue along the crease. Press the next strip in place with folds aligned. Repeat until all four of the layers are glued together. Re-crease all the layers together along the fold.

5. Loosely fold in half, ends together (don't crease) and fringe the layers, cutting to within ¾" of the fold.

6. Apply double sided tape to the top (handle) of the jug along the seam line and extend along the back. Adhere the fringe to make the top fin and tail for the fish.

7. Cut several colors of tissue paper into 4" squares. With your index finger in the center of a square, wrap the tissue paper around your finger. Dip the end into the glue and press on the side of the jug. Remove your finger and scrunch the tissue so it adheres securely in a compact "blossom" shape. Repeat, mixing colors, until the sides of the jug are covered.

8. Cut several strips of crepe paper streamers in varying colors and widths. Apply double sided tape to the bottom of the jug along the seam line, and press the ends of the streamers to it, overlapping as you go to accommodate as many streamers as you can.

9. Use paint pens to decorate the fish's snout and face.

10. Use a piece of yarn to loop through the jug handle to hang.

Bemiss-Jason Spectra® Construction Paper, Tissue Paper, Art Crepe™; Fiskars® Scissors; Elmer's® Craft Bond™ Tacky Paste, School Glue, 3D Paint Pens; Sakura of America Permapaque™ Opaque Paint Marker, Darice® Double Sided Tape

Cover labels with colored paper.

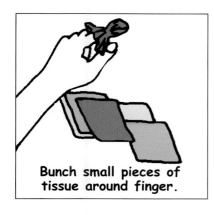

Bunch small pieces of tissue around finger.

Glue crumpled tissue to surface of bottle.

Glue streamers to bottle with double stick tape.

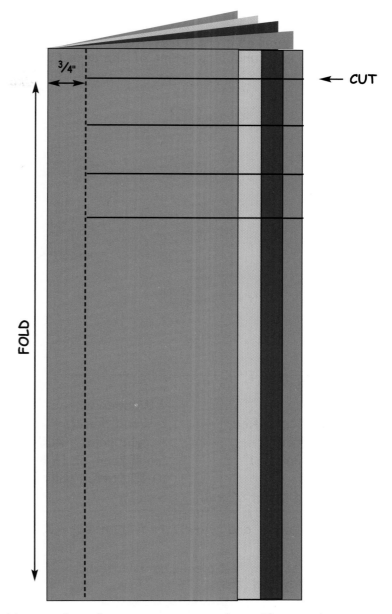

3/4"

← CUT

FOLD

Nest strips of crepe paper together. Glue at the fold line to secure. Cut from the edge to within 3/4" from the fold to fringe.

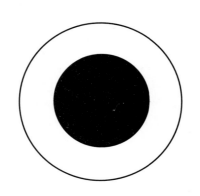

EYE PATTERN

CUT 2

Creeping Crab

by Zachary and Alexis Tschida

Crabs are remarkable creatures that hide from their predators in the crevices of the coral reef. Our crab is a fun look at some of the crab's physical characteristics.

You will need:

Felt - Red	4 Wooden wheels - 1"	Thick white glue
Large foam sheet - Red	2 Wood dowels - ¼" x 5¼"	Glue stick
2 Brass fasteners	Acrylic paint - Red	¼ hole punch"
2 Styrofoam balls - 1"	Small foam or flat paint brush	Ruler
2 Wiggly eyes - ½"	10-15 Cotton balls	Clothespins
Red cardboard about 5" x 8"	Stapler	Scissors

1. Paint the dowels and wheels red then set aside to dry.

2. Cut foam sheet and felt pieces as directed on pattern for body and legs.

3. Assemble claw pinchers by aligning the X's of parts 1 and 2 (with part 1 on top). Push a brass fastener through holes to connect. Remember to reverse the parts for the second set so your crab will have a right and left claw.

4. Glue one felt body piece over assembled legs and body. Let glue dry.

5. Place 10-15 cotton balls in center of body assembly. Run a thick bead of glue around the edge, and attach second felt body on top. Use clothespins to hold in place while glue dries.

6. Glue a wiggly eye to the center of each styrofoam ball for eyes. Let dry. Glue the eyes to the body. Let dry.

7. Apply glue to one long and both short edges of each eyelid then glue to body, wrapping and gluing around each eye.

8. Meanwhile, make the base by cutting a 5⅜" x 8⅛" rectangle from red construction paper and another from the tag board. Mark the 1⅛" lines and placement for punched holes on the tag board. Coat the other side of the tag board with the glue stick then glue the construction paper to it.

9. On the wrong side of the base, score along the marked lines using a ruler and point of the scissors. Punch holes and cut tabs as indicated. Glue end tabs to form box. Option: Cover a small gift box with red paper.

10. Insert dowels through holes. Ensure holes are large enough to allow the dowels to turn freely. Place wheels on ends of dowels.

11. Glue crab body to top of base.

Fiskars® Hole Punch, Ruler, Scissors; Bemiss-Jason Spectra® Construction Paper; Darice® Felt, Wiggly Eyes, Foamies™, Wood Wheels; Dow Styrofoam® Brand Plastic Foam; Forster® Dowels; Delta Ceramcoat® Acrylic Paint; Eagle® Paint Brush; Elmer's® Craft Bond™ Glue Stick, School Glue

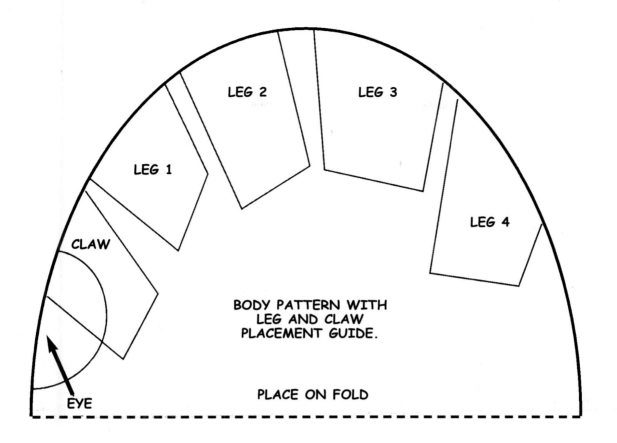

LEG 2

LEG 3

LEG 1

LEG 4

CLAW

BODY PATTERN WITH
LEG AND CLAW
PLACEMENT GUIDE.

PLACE ON FOLD

EYE

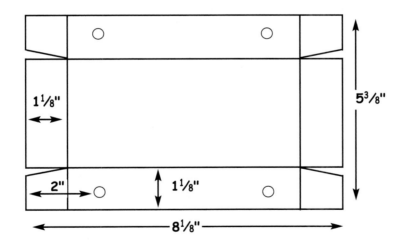

$1\frac{1}{8}$"

$5\frac{3}{8}$"

2"

$1\frac{1}{8}$"

$8\frac{1}{8}$"

Place crab shell on top of
box. Pad with cotton balls.

Place rubber band around
end of dowel to hold in place.

Push dowels through holes
in sides of box.

Hands On Crafts for Kids

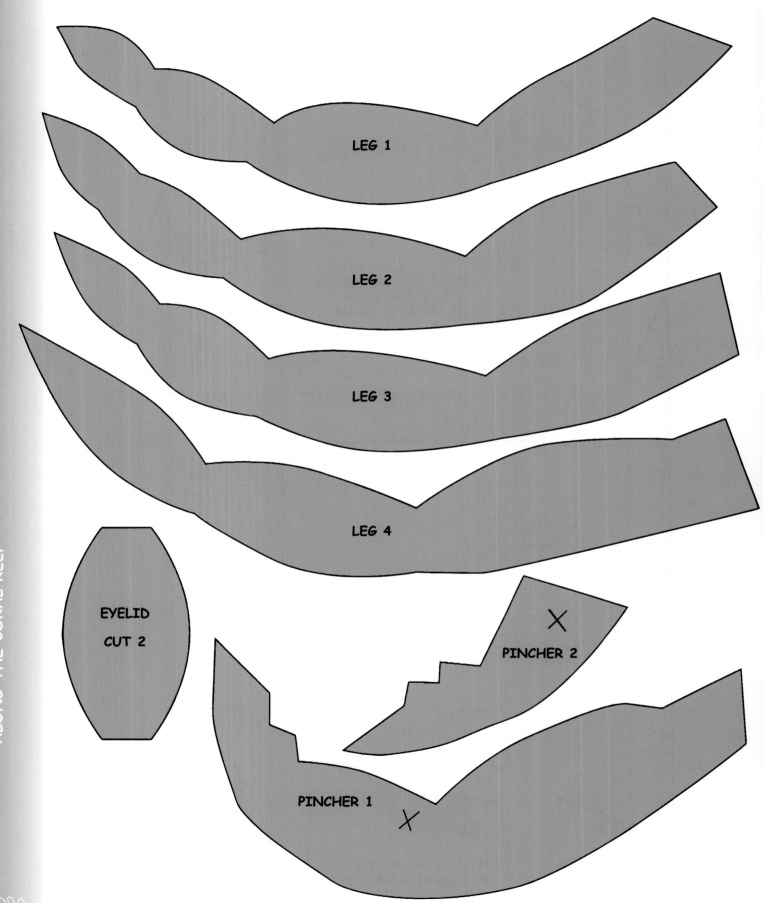

LEG 1

LEG 2

LEG 3

LEG 4

EYELID
CUT 2

PINCHER 2

PINCHER 1

Hands On Crafts for Kids

Sea Turtles

by Tracia Ledford Williams

These creatures frequent the warm water of the coral reef. The sea turtle is often green and has a large, streamlined shell and head and limbs that don't retract into its shell. Our turtle shell is actually a clay pot and a little cuter than most sea turtles you'd see in the wild.

You will need:
6" Clay saucer
Acrylic paint - Green, Yellow
  and Brown
Foam sheet - Green
Scissors
Craft sticks
Paint brush
Stencil sponges
Tacky paste
Black permanent pen
Pencil
Tracing paper

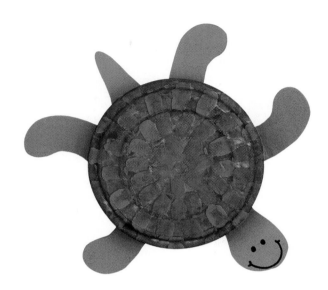

1. Cut stencil sponge into 4 pieces. Dip into green paint then apply over the bottom and sides of clay saucer. Dip sponge into yellow paint then apply some to the same area.

2. Dip a new sponge into brown paint and apply rectangles to the saucer, let dry.

3. Trace 4 feet patterns, 1 head pattern and 1 tail pattern to the green foam sheet, cut out.

Draw two eyes and a smile on the head with the black permanent pen.

4. Dip craft stick into paste, apply to foam pieces. Paste feet, tail, and head to saucer, creating the turtle.

Tip: Place a small clear plate on top of the saucer to make the turtle into a candy dish.

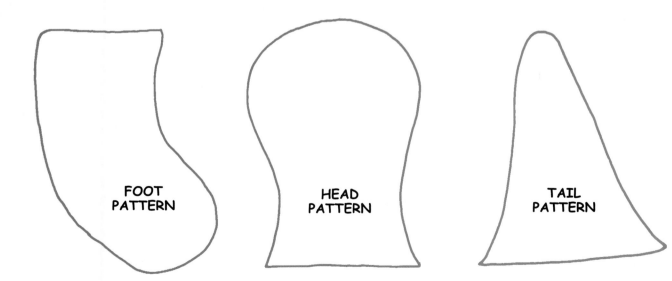

FOOT
PATTERN

HEAD
PATTERN

TAIL
PATTERN

Delta Ceramcoat® Acrylic Paint, Cherished Memories™ Stencil Buddy™, Stencil Sponges; Darice® Foamies™; Sakura of America IDenti-pen™; Elmer's® Craft Bond™ Tacky Paste; Forster® Craft Sticks; Fiskars® Scissors; Bemiss-Jason Tracing Paper

ALONG THE CORAL REEF

Hands On Crafts for Kids

101

Fish Spiral Mobile

by Sandi Genovese

A spiral mobile is a unique technique to display examples of fish which inhabit the coral reef. There are so many different species of fish on the reef because of the complexity of the ecosystem providing many ways for fish to feed and hunt.

You will need:
Die-cut machine or scissors
Dies - Small Crab, Tiny Fish, Small Octopus, Small Shark, Small Starfish, Small Stingray, Extra Large Spiral
Poster board - Blue
Construction paper - Red, Orange, Yellow, Gold, Light Brown, Dark Brown, Light Green, Dark Green, Blue, Purple, Gray and Black
Patterned paper
Self-adhesive colored paper
Red Ribbon
Hole punches - 1/16" and 1/8"
Fish craft punch, or stickers
Glue stick
White thread

1. Die-cut the spiral out of blue poster board, or use pattern and scissors. Using the 1/16" hole punch, cut holes in the spiral wherever you want elements to hang. Punch a 1/8" hole for the ribbon in the middle of the spiral that will suspend the entire mobile. Thread the ribbon through the hole.

2. Die-cut the stingray out of two shades of brown or use pattern and scissors. Use the perforation as a guide to trim the darker shade of brown wings and tail. Glue the darker brown parts to the lighter brown body. Repeat for the second stingray that is facing the opposite direction. Place a small strip of black paper behind the eye opening. Insert white thread between the pair of embellished stingrays then glue together.

3. Die-cut two sets of octopuses from two shades of green and purple. Draw the shading on the dark green for hair and trim. Attach the dark green to the light green octopus. Using the 1/16" hole punch, cut holes out of the light green octopus. Glue a piece of black behind the eyes. Glue the purple octopus behind. Make a second octopus then insert a piece of thread between the embellished die-cuts. Glue together. Repeat embellishing and inserting thread between each of the other pairs of sea creatures.

4. To finish the mobile, slide the thread of each of the creatures through the holes in the spiral leaving the extra thread. Adjust the thread as necessary. Glue fish punches over ends of thread to hold in place, or use stickers. Trim off extra thread.

Ellison® The XL Ellison® LetterMachine™, Decorative and Instructional Dies; Bemiss Jason Spectra® Construction Paper, Poster Board, Patterned Paper; Fiskars® Scissors, Craft Punches; Elmer's ® Craft Bond™ Glue Stick

Cut patterns in more than one color then layer patterns as shown.

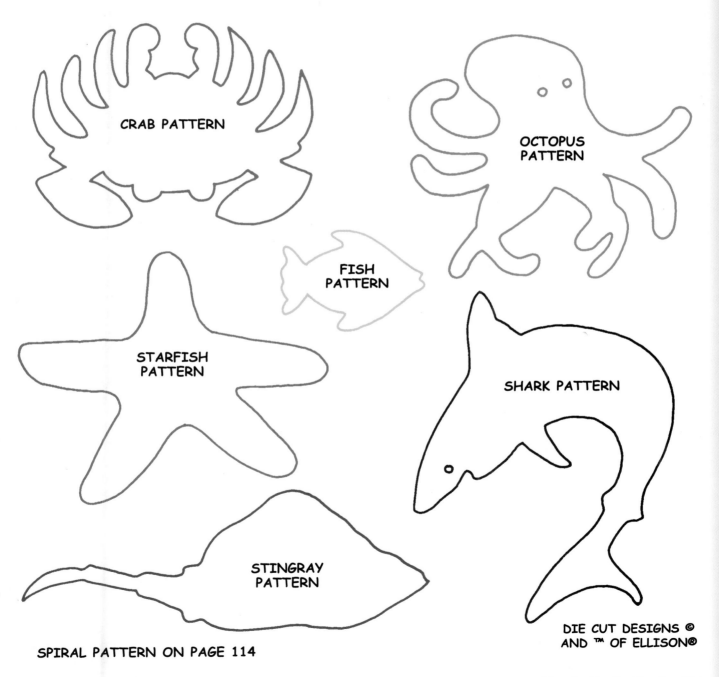

CRAB PATTERN

OCTOPUS PATTERN

FISH PATTERN

STARFISH PATTERN

SHARK PATTERN

STINGRAY PATTERN

SPIRAL PATTERN ON PAGE 114

Sea Anemone Bouquet

by Patty Cox

These unique creatures are often attached to rocks or coral. They look a lot like bunches of the pink and purple petals of the anemone wild flower. The petals are really arms or tentacles to capture food.

You will need:
Foam sheets - Pink, Purple or Blue
$5\frac{7}{8}$" x $\frac{13}{16}$" Styrofoam disk
Iridescent sequins
Iridescent acrylic beads
Pearl fish pony beads
Wavy ridged paper - Natural
Chenille stems - Peach
22 Gauge wire
$\frac{1}{2}$" sequin pins, straight pins
Double-sided tape
$8\frac{1}{2}$" x 4" Adhesive sheet
Small rubberbands
Hot water, covered pan
10 $\frac{1}{4}$ oz. Soup can
White glue
Scissors
Optional: Sea spray potpourri oil

1. Use the basic body pattern to make your first anemone from a foam sheet. Other anemones can be taller, fatter or have more fringed arms as desired.

2. Cut the 1" edge into narrow fringe. Stretch the bottom edge for a different look.

3. Starting at the unfringed edge, roll foam into a tube. Glue end or adhere with a strip of double-sided tape.

4. To keeps arms from standing straight up, pull arms down around body and hold in place with a rubberband. Put anemones in a covered pan of hot water (steaming, but not boiling) for about 15 minutes. Remove from water. Let cool on a paper towel then remove rubberbands.

5. Add sequins or beads to body with sequin pins or attach with glue, using straight pins to hold in place.

6. Cut an $8\frac{1}{2}$" x $5\frac{1}{4}$" piece of craft foam. Fringe 1" along one long edge. Stick foam around soup can with double-adhesive. Glue sequins around the sides.

7. Cut $5\frac{5}{8}$" circles from wavy ridge paper. Cut a circle from center the same size as the base of the can. Cut two $1\frac{1}{4}$" x 1" strips from wavy ridge paper. Glue circle to styrofoam. Glue strips to sides. Secure paper to styrofoam with straight pins. This will be your sea floor base.

8. Using a pencil eraser, press a recessed area in styrofoam about $\frac{1}{4}$" deep and large enough to hold the soup can. Glue covered soup can into the center hole.

9. Glue and pin anemones around can on sea floor base.

10. Bend chenille stems with 5 or more "fingers" to form coral. Twist each finger together. Stick bottom point into styrofoam base around anemones.

11. Glue or wire fish beads on base, can or anemones.

Optional: Drip sea spray potpourri oil in the center of each anemone.

Bemiss Jason Mini Flute Corobuff® Sheets;
Darice® Foamies™, Sequin pins, Iridescent Sequins and Beads, Chenille Stems, Wire, Double Sided Tape; Dow Styrofoam® Brand Plastic Foam; Elmer's® White School Glue; Fiskars® Scissors

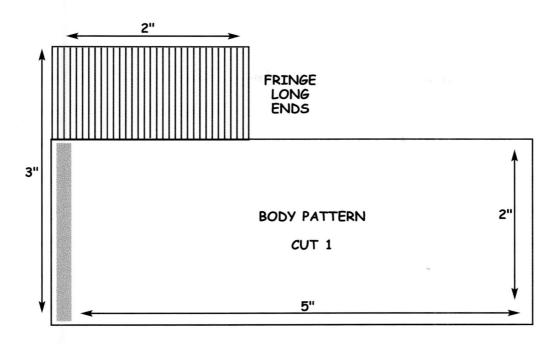

2"

FRINGE
LONG
ENDS

3"

BODY PATTERN

CUT 1

2"

5"

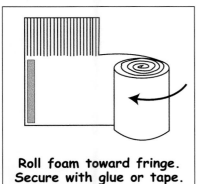

Roll foam toward fringe.
Secure with glue or tape.

Pull fringe down over roll.
Secure with rubber band.

Remove fringe then
decorate base with sequins.

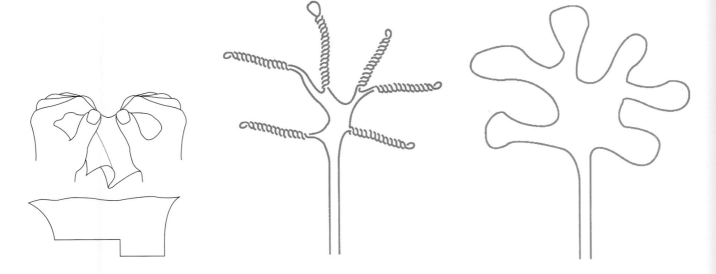

OPTIONAL: Stretch lower edge of foam for a different shape. Form different colored chenille stems into shapes of coral then place in center of arrangement.

Embossed Foil Sun

by Cindy Gorder

What could be more important to life on earth than the sun. This foil and styrofoam sun is a beautiful tribute to this important celestial body.

You will need:
8" diameter Styrofoam disk
Foam sheet - any color
Metallic Gold paper
Heavy duty aluminum foil
Stiff twine
Glue
Straight pins
Scissors
Oil pastels - black
Paper hologram twists - 4 Silver, 2 Gold
Decorative edge scissors
Paper crimper
Dowel or pencil
Tweezers

1. Trace around the styrofoam disk to make a circle from the foam sheet. Cut out and set aside.

2. Draw a face on the styrofoam. Working on one facial element at a time, draw a line of glue on the design and apply a piece of twine to the glue. Use straight pins to hold twine in place until the glue dries. Hint: it may be necessary to use tweezers to remove pins, while holding the twine securely to the styrofoam.

3. Use a scrap piece of styrofoam to sand the top edge of the disk.

4. Cut a piece of aluminum foil large enough to wrap around the disk. Lightly cover the entire surface of the dull side of the foil with black oil pastel.

5. Lay the foil over the twine features on the styrofoam then starting in the center of the face, carefully and gently push the foil against the raised twine areas. Work the foil into the crevices and around the twine. Wrap to the back of the disk. To smooth the edges, roll the disk along a tabletop. Use a paper towel to rub some of the oil pastel away. Smooth the flat parts of the foil against the styrofoam.

6. Fold the metallic gold paper in half (colored sides together) then fold again to make four equal divisions. Draw ray shapes as shown in the diagram. Cut with decorative edge scissors. Run rays through the paper crimper. Cut 8 more rays from foil and crimp.

7. Arrange the rays on the foam disk; first the gold, then the foil. Glue in place.

8. Fold the twists in half and run the outer ends partway through the paper crimper, leaving the center uncrimped. Unfold then twist the ends around a pencil or dowel. Arrange on disk with the gold and foil rays then glue in place.

9. Cut a circle from the foam the same size as the styrofoam. Apply a generous amount of glue to the foam circle then carefully position it on top of the styrofoam disk, trapping the rays and twists inbetween. Put a few books or similar weight on top and let dry.

10. Glue a loop of twine near the top for a hanger.

Dow Styrofoam® Brand Plastic Foam; Darice® Twine, Foamies™; Fiskars® Paper Edgers, Paper Crimper, Scissors; Forster® Dowel; Sakura of America Cray-Pas® Junior Artist Oil Pastels; Bemiss-Jason Fadeless® Paper, Art Fun™ Twists; Elmer's® White School glue

MOTHER EARTH

EMBOSSED SUN
PATTERN

Press foil onto surface
over the pattern.

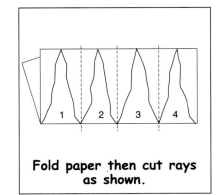

1 2 3 4

Fold paper then cut rays
as shown.

Glue rays to back of
styrofoam disk then foam
circle on top of rays.

Sundial

by Paula and Ken Moliver

Telling time is easy, even without a watch if you have our outdoor foam sundial. Ancient civilizations used this method of watching shadows to determine the time of day.

You will need:
Acrylic paint - Brown, Dark Brown, Dark
   Green, Bright Green, Light Green,
   Blue and Light Blue
Foam sheets - assorted colors
Satin varnish
Styrofoam sheet 10" x 12" x 1¼" thick
Stipple paint brush
5/16" Dowel - 12"
Assorted precut, pairs of foam shapes -
   flowers, etc.
Double sided tape
Protractor
Rubber band
Black permanent pen
Pencil
Straight pins

1. Draw pattern on top of sundial as shown.

2. Squeeze out paint then use the stipple paintbrush to dab onto styrofoam top. Use blue and light blue paint for the water. Brown and dark brown paint are for the path. Use dark green, bright green, and light green paint for grass. Carry design out over the sides of Styrofoam. Paint "N" as seen in diagram.

3. After paint dries, varnish all painted surfaces. Let dry.

4. Use a protractor to draw the circle. Mark center dot and 180° on both sides. Use the black permanent pen to write numbers as shown using protractor to space evenly.

5. Using double sided tape, tape matching shapes together with a toothpick between. Push into styrofoam.

6. Push pencil point through board at center of dial then replace with dowel. This is your gnomon. Tape 3 cutout foam suns together and slip onto top of the gnomon.

7. Adjust angle of the sundial base to match up with your latitude and point the painted "N" to the north.

8. To find the correct angle of the sundial base, look on a map of where you live to find the latitude (lines on a map parallel to the equator). With the base of a protractor on the ground, adjust the board until you reach the angle of your latitude. Place a tight rubber band on the dowel under the base to hold it in place. Place it in your garden and enjoy the hours spent with nature.

Delta Ceramcoat® Acrylic Paint, Ceramcoat® Exterior/Interior Satin Varnish;
Dow Styrofoam® Brand Plastic Foam; Eagle® Stipple Paint Brush; Forster® Dowel; Darice® Foamies™,
Double Sided Tape; Fiskars® Protractor; Sakura of America IDenti-pen™

MOTHER EARTH

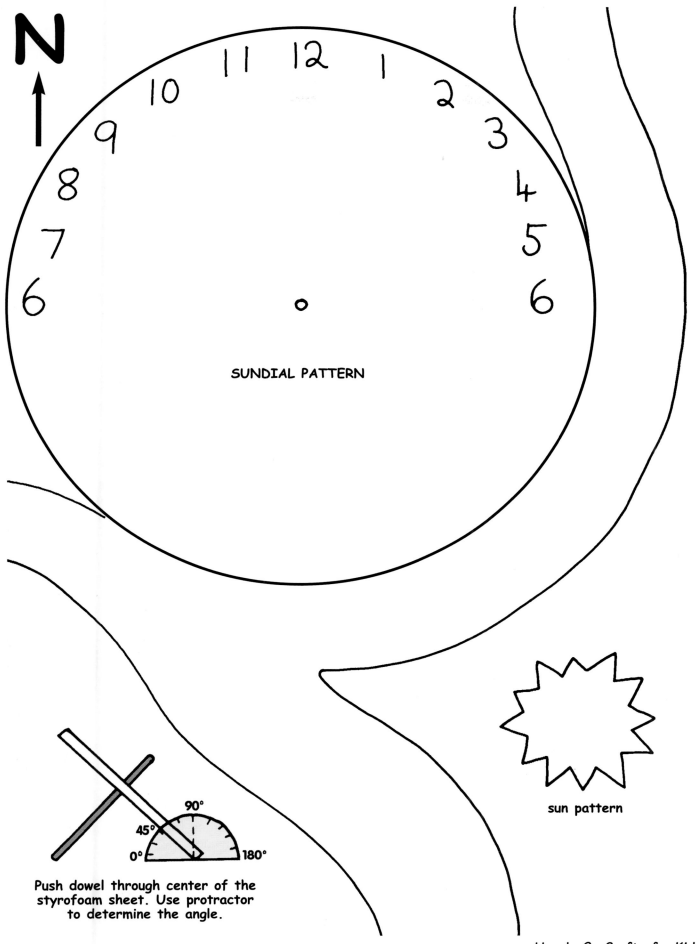

N

SUNDIAL PATTERN

10 11 12 1 2 3 4 5 6
9 8 7 6

sun pattern

90°
45°
0° 180°

Push dowel through center of the
styrofoam sheet. Use protractor
to determine the angle.

Hands On Crafts for Kids

Earth Symbols
by Dimensions®

Make beaded symbols of the earth, stars and planets with a simple iron on technique.

You will need:
Pegboards - square, circle, star
Ironing paper
Neon Perler beads - Yellow, Orange, and Pink
Transparent Perler beads - Purple, Turquoise and Green
Plain Perler Beads - Yellow
Paper clips
Thread - any color
Scissors
Cardboard
Household iron

1. Place beads one by one on the pegboards following patterns.

2. Preheat the iron to the medium setting. When carrying the bead design to the iron, be careful not to tip or bump the beads from the pegboard. Cover the beads with the ironing paper. Keeping the iron level, gently iron all areas of the beads in a circular motion for about 30 seconds to fuse the beads evenly. Once the design is cool, peel off the ironing paper.

3. Place a piece of stiff cardboard on top of the design and flip everything over. Lift off the pegboard. Cover the design with the ironing paper and iron the other side to fuse it evenly.

4. Once you have made all the designs, bend the paper clips open. Cut your thread into pieces of different lengths. Tie a few of the threads to the paper clips. Tie the other end of the thread through your designs. Hang some of the small designs from the larger ones with more thread.

Place ironing paper over beads. Fuse beads together by going over surface with iron.

Dimensions® Perler® Beads, Perler® Pegboards, Perler® Ironing Paper; Fiskars® Scissors

EARTH SYMBOLS
PATTERNS

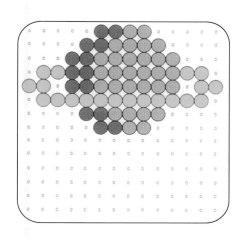

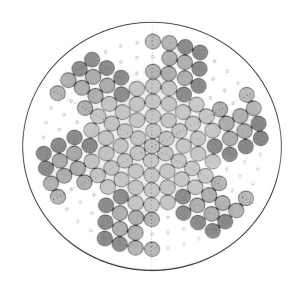

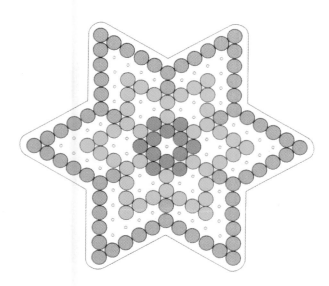

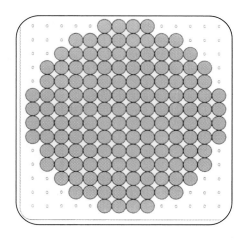

Unbend paper clips. Tie one end of thread to earth symbols and the opposite end to the paper clip. Keep attaching paper clips and earth symbols to make mobile.

Seed and Salt Bucket
by Tracia Ledford Williams

Create a useful bucket to store both seeds for the birds and salt for icy sidewalks.

You will need:
Galvanized bucket
Acrylic paint - White, Fuchsia, Black, Medium Blue, Tangerine, Yellow, Green, Light Green and Opaque Red
Brush on metal primer
Matte varnish
Round paint brushes - #8 and #4
1" Sponge brush
Tracing paper
Pencil
Paper towel

1. Apply metal primer over entire surface of bucket, inside and out, using the sponge brush. Let dry.

2. Trace and transfer patterns onto each side of the bucket.

3. Paint the snowman white. Use medium blue to paint scarf around his neck and tangerine paint for his nose. Using a small piece of crumpled up paper towel, dip softly into white paint and add snowy background around snowman. Add black eyes, mouth, outline of arms and buttons to the snowman. Using the opaque red paint, add some red hearts.

4. Using medium blue, paint the blue bird on the opposite side of the bucket. Add the beak and legs with yellow paint. Paint leaves and vines using green, add lines of light green for highlights. Add black dot to eyes. Mix a tiny bit of white to medium blue paint and add strokes for feathers on the bird.

5. Let paint dry. Finish with 2 coats of varnish, allowing each coat to dry between applications.

SNOWMAN HEAD PATTERN

BIRD PATTERN

MOTHER EARTH

Delta Ceramcoat® Metal Primer, Ceramcoat®Acrylic Paint, Ceramcoat® Exterior/Interior Matte Varnish; Eagle® Brush Kid's Are Painter's Too Paint Brushes

Mother Earth Suet Holder

by Lynda Musante

One of the "duties" of Mother Earth is to provide food for the wildlife of the world. Our wire holder will feed the wildlife in your own garden or backyard.

You will need:
3" Wooden disk
3 Plastic coated wire hangers
16 Gauge wire
Plastic container or used
  margarine tub
Nail
Craft snips
Sand paper
White glue
Bird seed
Pine cone
Peanut butter

1. Sand disk smooth. Spread glue on disk to seal wood. Allow to dry.

2. To make wings, squeeze the hanger hook of one hanger closed. Pull the center of the hanger up to the hook of the hanger and loop it into the twisted section to secure. Bend hook over the loop.

3. To assemble the body, straighten the hooks on two hangers and bend them at a right angle. They will become the arms. Insert one hanger crossways into the second hanger. Bend both arms forward. Cut a 12" length of wire. Hold wings in position and wrap wire around all three hanger's twisted sections to secure.

4. Pull down the wide section of the two body hangers and flatten center area. Use nail to poke two holes 1" apart at the center point on each side of the plastic container bottom. Cut four 3" lengths of wire and bend each piece into a "U" shape. Insert a wire "U" through one set of holes and position container over bent hanger. Twist wire to secure it to the hanger. Repeat with three other sides.

5. Fill container with birdseed. Spread a pinecone with peanut butter then squeeze arms together to hold it. Your bird feeder can stand in the garden or hang.

6. Glue disk to top for face.

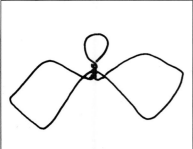

Fold bottom of hangar up over hook to make wings.

Shape hook and hangar to make arms and body.

Attach food dish to bottom of hangars with wire.

Darice® Wire, Wooden Disk; Fiskars® Softouch® Craft Snips; Elmer's® School Glue

MOTHER EARTH

SPIRAL PATTERN
FOR FISH SPIRAL MOBILE
(Page 102)

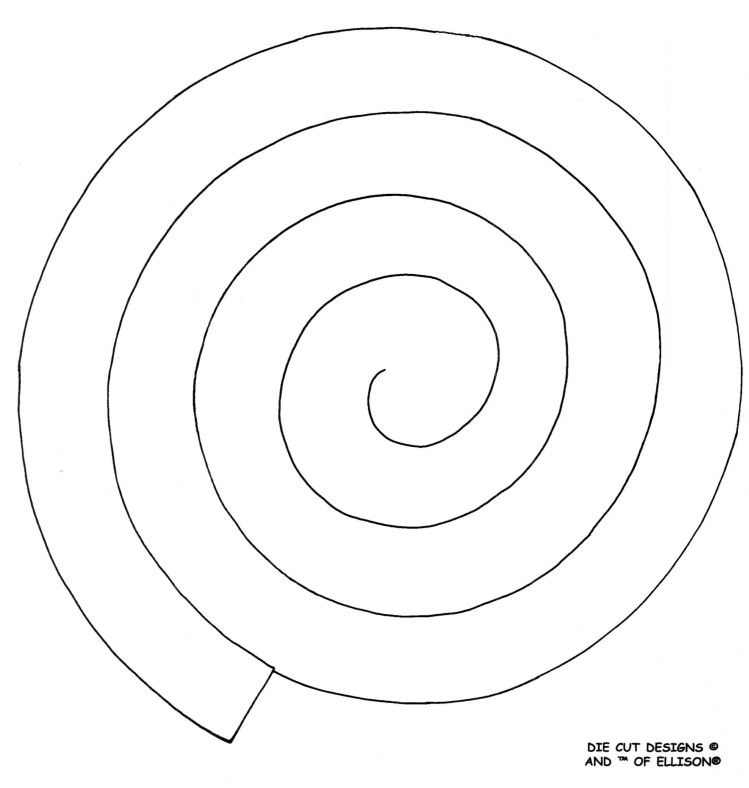

DIE CUT DESIGNS ©
AND ™ OF ELLISON®